D1497429

RIDDLES OF THE SPHINX

And Other Mathematical Puzzle Tales

NEW MATHEMATICAL LIBRARY

The New Mathematical Library (NML) was started in 1961 by the School Mathematics Study Group to make available to high school students short expository books on various topics not usually covered in the high school syllabus. In a decade the NML matured into a steadily growing series of some twenty titles of interest not only to the originally intended audience, but to college students and teachers at all levels. Previously published by Random House and L. W. Singer, the NML became a publication series of the Mathematical Association of America (MAA) in 1975. Under the auspices of the MAA the NML continues to grow and remains dedicated to its original and expanded purposes. In its third decade, it contains some thirty titles.

RIDDLES OF THE SPHINX

And Other Mathematical Puzzle Tales

by

Martin Gardner

 New Mathematical Library, Volume 32

Published by The Mathematical Association of America

Technical drawings by Kelly Solis-Navarro

Cartoons by John Johnson

Set in ten point Laurel type

by Science Typographers, Inc.

Second Printing

© 1987 by the Mathematical Association of America (Inc.)

All rights reserved under International Pan-American Copyright Conventions.

Published in Washington, D.C. by

The Mathematical Association of America

Library of Congress Catalog Card Number 87-062657

Complete Set ISBN: 0-88385-600-X

Vol. 32 ISBN: 0-88385-632-8 (soft cover)

ISBN: 0-88385-633-6 (hard cover)

Copyright 1988

Manufactured in the United States of America

Editors' Preface

This book, in many ways, is a departure from the traditional New Mathematical Library (NML) offering. While most NML volumes are aimed at readers interested in exploring particular mathematical topics, this volume is likely to appeal also to puzzle solvers, science fiction fans, and, of course, to the many admirers of Martin Gardner's charming exposition.

We, the editors, have been intrigued with some of the mathematics contained in these riddles; we are most grateful to the author for having permitted and actively contributed to elaborations and extensions of a number of mathematical gems encapsuled in his riddles. We hope that science fiction fans who are not yet hooked on mathematics will become interested and will find mathematics stranger than fiction, even science fiction.

The Editors

September 1987

New Mathematical Library Editorial Committee

Ivan Niven, Chairman,
University of Oregon

Anneli Lax, Editor,
New York University

Donald J. Albers, Menlo College
Joanne Elliott, Rutgers University
Basil Gordon, University of California
Herbert J. Greenberg, University of Denver
Peter Ungar, Emeritus, New York University

NEW MATHEMATICAL LIBRARY

1 Numbers: Rational and Irrational *by Ivan Niven*
2 What is Calculus About? *by W. W. Sawyer*
3 An Introduction to Inequalities *by E. F. Beckenbach and R. Bellman*
4 Geometric Inequalities *by N. D. Kazarinoff*
5 The Contest Problem Book I Annual High School Mathematics Examinations 1950–1960. Compiled and with solutions *by Charles T. Salkind*
6 The Lore of Large Numbers, *by P. J. Davis*
7 Uses of Infinity *by Leo Zippin*
8 Geometric Transformations I *by I. M. Yaglom, translated by A. Shields*
9 Continued Fractions *by Carl D. Olds*
10 Graphs and Their Uses *by Oystein Ore* (revised, see Volume 34) .
11 ⎫ Hungarian Problem Books I and II, Based on the Eötvös
12 ⎭ Competitions 1894–1905 and 1906–1928, *translated by E. Rapaport*
13 Episodes from the Early History of Mathematics *by A. Aaboe*
14 Groups and Their Graphs *by I. Grossman and W. Magnus*
15 The Mathematics of Choice *by Ivan Niven*
16 From Pythagoras to Einstein *by K. O. Friedrichs*
17 The Contest Problem Book II Annual High School Mathematics Examinations 1961–1965. Compiled and with solutions *by Charles T. Salkind*
18 First Concepts of Topology *by W. G. Chinn and N. E. Steenrod*
19 Geometry Revisited *by H. S. M. Coxeter and S. L. Greitzer*
20 Invitation to Number Theory *by Oystein Ore*
21 Geometric Transformations II *by I. M. Yaglom, translated by A. Shields*
22 Elementary Cryptanalysis—A Mathematical Approach *by A. Sinkov*
23 Ingenuity in Mathematics *by Ross Honsberger*
24 Geometric Transformations III *by I. M. Yaglom, translated by A. Shenitzer*
25 The Contest Problem Book III Annual High School Mathematics Examinations 1966–1972. Compiled and with solutions *by C. T. Salkind and J. M. Earl*
26 Mathematical Methods in Science *by George Pólya*
27 International Mathematical Olympiads—1959–1977. Compiled and with solutions *by S. L. Greitzer*
28 The Mathematics of Games and Gambling *by Edward W. Packel*
29 The Contest Problem Book IV Annual High School Mathematics Examinations 1973–1982. Compiled and with solutions *by R. A. Artino, A. M. Gaglione and N. Shell*
30 The Role of Mathematics in Science *by M. M. Schiffer and L. Bowden*
31 International Mathematical Olympiads 1978–1985 and forty supplementary problems. Compiled and with solutions by *Murray S. Klamkin.*
32 Riddles of the Sphinx *by Martin Gardner*
33 U.S.A. Mathematical Olympiads 1972–1986. Compiled and with solutions by *Murray S. Klamkin.*
34 Graphs and Their Uses, *by Oystein Ore*. Revised and updated *by Robin J. Wilson.*

Other titles in preparation.

FOREWORD

This is the third and final collection of puzzle columns that I contributed to *Isaac Asimov's Science Fiction Magazine* over a period of about ten years. The format follows that of two previous anthologies: *Science Fiction Puzzle Tales* (1981) and *Puzzles from Other Worlds* (1984).

Each chapter poses a problem answered in the First Answers section. The solution in turn raises another problem that is solved in the Second Answers section. This may suggest a third question, and in several instances there is a fourth. Material has been added based on letters from readers of Asimov's magazine, material from my files, and suggestions from others listed below.

Many of the problems lead into nontrivial regions of mathematics and science. Whether or not these puzzles have deeper roots, I hope readers will find them entertaining, and enjoy the opportunity to exercise their wits.

I wish particularly to thank Peter Ungar for going so painstakingly through the manuscript and adding fascinating new material, and Anneli Lax for her superb editing and production work. I am indebted also to Basil Gordon and Richard Guy for numerous corrections and excellent suggestions, and to Peter Renz for suggesting the MAA as a publisher, finding ideal illustrators, for general supervision of the book's production, and for providing valuable input in many ways.

Martin Gardner

For Solomon W. Golomb

Whose great creative ingenuity continues to be an
unending source of elegant mathematical surprises.

CONTENTS

RIDDLES

FIRST ANSWERS

SECOND ANSWERS

THIRD ANSWERS

FOURTH ANSWERS

PRIMITIVE REP-TILE

1 RIDDLES OF THE SPHINX

Dr. Mitsu Matsu, the world-renowned genetic engineer, was the first to construct two-dimensional life forms. Well, not exactly two dimensional, but almost. They are crystal-like microorganisms that flourish in monolayer cultures, that is, cultures only one molecule thick.

Matsu called his organisms "rep-tiles" for two reasons: they replicate themselves, and they are shaped like polygonal tiles. All rep-tiles are much too small to be visible except in powerful neutrino microscopes. They slowly swim about through the mono-layer liquid by means of tiny cilia on their borders and obtain food by absorbing it through their "skin." As a rep-tile grows, it preserves its polygonal shape. When it reaches a critical size, it splits not in half, like an amoeba, but into four smaller congruent tiles, each similar to the original. The four newly "born" rep-tiles need not be of the same "handedness" as the original. That is, one or more of the four may be mirror images of the original.

At first, Matsu was able to create rep-tiles only in the shapes of triangles and squares. It is easy to see how any triangle T can be divided into four smaller triangles, congruent to each other and similar to T, and how parallelograms can be split into four smaller similar parallelograms.

Several months later he managed to produce three other rep-tiles, each with four sides, and three six-sided rep-tiles. They are shown below.

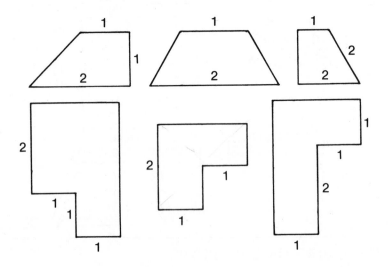

How quickly can you draw lines on each of these six shapes to show how they replicate by splitting into four congruent parts, each the same shape as the original? Solutions are given in the First Answers section.

2 PRECOGNITION AND THE MYSTIC SEVEN

Here is a group of remarkable number tricks that will amaze you when done on any small calculator. Before reading further, obtain a pocket or desk calculator and take the tricks as they come. All of them involve the number 7, the digit that ancient and medieval mystics believed to be unusually rich in magical properties. Although you will be asked to select certain numbers at random, I will exercise my paranormal powers of precognition and try to predict, in each case, the exact outcome of your calculations.

As a starter, put into the readout the mysterious number 15873. Select any digit from 1 through 9 and multiply 15873 by that digit. Now multiply the product by 7. The readout will show your chosen digit repeated six times.

Why does it work? Because 15873 times 7 is 111111, and 111111 times any digit will naturally produce that digit repeated six times. To get a longer string of digits, multiply 12345679 (note that 8 is omitted) by any positive digit, then multiply by 9. This works because 12345679 times 9 is 111111111.

Let's try something not quite so easy to explain. Assuming you are older than 9 and younger than 100, put your age in the readout. Multiply it by the magic number 1443, then multiply the result by 7. The surprising result: your age repeated three times!

This always works because 1443 times 7 is 10101. It is easy to see that any two-digit number multiplied by 10101 will produce a triple "stutter" of the two-digit number.

A trick closely related to the previous one starts by putting any three-digit number in the readout. Hit the same three keys in the same order so that the readout stutters. In other words, the readout contains a six-digit number of the form *ABCABC*, where *A*, *B* and *C* need not be different digits. Divide this by 13. There will be no remainder. Divide again by 11. Again no remainder! Now divide by 7 and take a look at the readout. It is your original three-digit number!

To understand why this works, multiply 7 by 11 and then by 13. The product is 1001. Obviously 1001 times any number *ABC* will give *ABCABC*. The trick simply reverses this process. *ABCABC* divided by 7, 11, and 13 (which is the same as dividing by 1001) must give *ABC*. It is easy to generalize to larger stuttering numbers. Do you see why a number of the form *ABCDABCD* becomes *ABCD* when divided by 137, then by 73?

For the next trick, put 999999 in the readout. Roll a die to get a number from 1 through 6. If you don't have a die handy, just roll an imaginary die and use whatever number comes up. Multiply 999999 by the randomly chosen digit, then divide the result by 7. Turn to the First Answers section to see what I predict about the final outcome.

3 ON TO CHARMIAN

It was early in 1983 that IRAS (Infrared Astronomy Satellite) was launched. Information from the satellite created something of a stir later that year when it suggested that a swarm of unidentified objects, possibly a planetary system, was orbiting the star Vega. IRAS II created a much bigger stir late in 1998 when it reported evidence of a tenth planet, moving in a highly eccentric orbit, far beyond the path of Pluto.

Was it really a planet? Some astronomers argued it was more likely a cluster of asteroids, others that it was a tiny black hole. It was not until many decades later that the spaceship *Bagel*, on one if its missions to the fringes of the solar system, finally confirmed that the object was indeed a planet.

The planet had earlier been named Iras, after the acronym of the satellite that first discovered it. Iras turned out to have a size and mass slightly larger than Mars, but smaller than Venus. While the *Bagel* was circling it, taking measurements of its size, rotation, orbital direction and velocity, and photographing its icy surface, Tanya occupied herself with some word play involving the planetary names. Tanya was the teen-age daughter of Colonel Ronald Couth, the officer in charge of the ship's computer.

First Tanya tried finding anagrams for the names of the planets, but none was very interesting. The letters of MARS rearranged to make ARMS and RAMS, EARTH became HEART, IRAS backward was SARI, and by changing the T of SATURN to U, the letters spelled URANUS.

Tanya next tried listing the initial letters of the planets in their order from the sun: MVEMJSUNPI, and was startled to see the word SUN formed by consecutive letters. She was even more surprised when she listed the planets in order of size or mass (both properties give the same ordering)—PMMIVEUNSJ. Do you see the beautiful coincidence? The five consecutive letters VEUNS spell VENUS if you simply switch U and N!

When Tanya's father walked into the computer shack, Tanya was amusing herself by making lists of ten words that suggested the planets in order from the sun—for example, thermometer, armless, dirt, war, lightning, rings, and so on.

"Working on anything unusual?" Couth asked.

"Not really. I've been playing with the names of the planets when I arrange them according to some property such as size or distance from the sun."

"Have you heard of the Erdös-Szekeres theorem?"

Tanya shook her head.

"I can best explain it in terms of a row of 10 soldiers, no two the same height." They could line up in order of ascending height, or in order of descending height, or in any other order. The theorem says that no matter what the order, there will always be at least four among the ten, not necessarily standing next to each other, who will be in ascending or in descending order. Furthermore, there are arrangements in which no five are in either ascending or descending order.

In general terms, the theorem says this. Let n be any positive integer. Let k be the smallest positive integer whose square is at least n. Then a sequence of n different numbers always has a monotonic (i.e. increasing or decreasing) subsequence of length k, and for every n there are sequences which do not have a monotonic subsequence of length $k + 1$.

"I understand," said Tanya. "What an elegant little theorem! It tells me that if I order nine planets in any way, at least three of them will be in increasing or in decreasing order with respect to size, and at least three will be in order of increasing or decreasing distance from the Sun, and at

least three will be in order of increasing or decreasing distance from
Earth."

"Precisely."

Tanya found a deck of cards and removed nine cards with values of
ace through nine. She wanted to see if she could arrange them so that no
four cards formed a monotonic sequence. First she tried 647193825. For a
moment she thought she had it. No—6432 was a descending subsequence.
Actually there are 84 ways to do it. In general, the number of ways is

$$2(k^2)! \prod_{i=0}^{k-1} \frac{i!}{(k+i)!}.$$

1. See if you can discover one of them.

2. How many different numberings of the planets do we have to
provide to be sure that, if the planets are ordered alphabetically, there will
be four planets whose numbers, in at least one numbering, form a
monotonic sequence?

4 TECHNOLOGY ON VZIGS

As all hard-nosed UFO astronauts know, higher intelligences than
ours have been exploring planetary civilizations throughout the galaxy for
millions of years. Here are some excerpts from a report stored in the
memory banks of a vast computer on a planet far from earth.

"Inhabitants of the planet VZIGS, orbiting the star HFM, have developed a technology that is extraordinary in the way portions of it have been simplified. Many of their machines operate on extremely low energy inputs, and are virtually free of maintenance problems.

1. The sides of dwellings are constructed from congruent modular units in the shapes of rectangular parallelepipeds that are joined to form regular three-dimensional space tesselations. Units with edge ratios roughly in the sequence $2:3:6$ are fastened together with strong adhesives. Units with more extreme ratios, made of soft organic material, are also used. These are joined by means of small metallic cylinders with a cone at one end and a flattened disk at the other. The cylinders are forced through the units by primitive percussion devices.

2. Clothing is periodically cleaned by an ingenious mechanism that subjects wet cloth to alternate compressions and expansions by moving the material laterally along a surface with an approximate sine-wave cross section. The device requires no electromagnetic energy, and has no moving parts.

3. Wet clothing is dried by an even simpler mechanism, also free of moving parts. No energy is required other than that produced by natural movements of the planet's atmosphere. The device is essentially a long, flexible cylinder.

4. It seems to be necessary for the creatures of planet VZIGS to keep their food preserved in a moderately cold state. This is done by a machine based solely on the fact that heat is absorbed when a substance changes from solid to liquid state. Again, the apparatus has been simplified so that the only moving parts are panels that open and close to provide access to the mechanism's interior.

5. Mathematical calculations and symbol processing are habitually performed by a device of incredible simplicity. It is small and portable, uses no energy, and emits no radiation. The operation is almost silent. It is capable of printing the symbols of all the languages spoken by the many species of intelligent protein-based life that flourish on the planet, as well as any desired graphic display. We recommend that the Supreme Council consider the potential usefulness of such a device in the teaching of our children.

6. One of the strangest aspects of the technology of planet VZIGS is that its principal transportation machine, not only for the creatures themselves but also for materials they desire to be moved from one place to another—is enormously complex. Instead of wheels, it utilizes cumbersome and needlessly intricate levers. The four independent sets of linked

levers are operated by sophisticated devices that contract and expand in ways that apparently are controlled by a small computer at the top of the vehicle. The machine clearly operates by the burning of fuel. The fuel enters through an opening at the front, and, as on our ancient spaceships, gas and residues are forced out through a similar aperture at the back. The machine is fitted with perceptrons which for some unknown reason are mounted on left and right sides rather than facing forward. The perceptrons guide the vehicle along any desired path. Movement is slow, but the machine is capable of varying speeds.

7. Another peculiarity that we observed about the life forms of VZIGS is that its more intelligent species are constantly exchanging circular objects of varying size and made of different kinds of metals and alloys. Most of them bear bas-relief portraits of their leaders. The creatures also seem to enjoy producing millions of tiny rectangular engravings, displaying pictures in full color of life forms and other objects. These are fastened to larger rectangular objects which are periodically pushed into containers, then distributed to other spots on the planet.

8. Our observations of the behavior of the creatures has established numerous other incomprehensible practices, of which we will here cite only two:

At periodic intervals, when not lying in dormant states of brief hibernation, the creatures insert a cylindrical object into their fuel-intake aperture and set fire to it. They allow it to burn almost completely before discarding it. We have been unable to determine the purpose of this bizarre custom.

At unpredictable moments, one of the creatures will be seized by a sudden paroxysm. A loud explosive noise, often repeated two or more times, accompanies a sudden expulsion of air from a curiously shaped protuberance located between the perceptrons and the creature's fuel-intake opening."

It should not be difficult to guess what the memo is all about. If it still puzzles you, turn to the First Answers section.

What is it?
Where did it come from?
Why is it here?
Read on, and some of these
questions will be answered.

5 THE VALLEY OF LOST THINGS

To mordant Ambrose Bierce
Life was fantastically perilous and fierce.
In Mexico, with not unfitting grotesquerie,
He

—Paul Curry Steele

Dot and Tot of Merryland is one of L. Frank Baum's long out-of-print juvenile fantasies. As a child in upstate New York, Baum had probably heard of a place called Maryland that could be reached by sailing down the Hudson River, then moving farther south along the coast. At any rate, his fantasy involves Tot, a small boy, and Dot, his slightly older friend. While the two children are playing in a rowboat, it breaks its moorings and floats down the river to Merryland.

The queen of Merryland is a doll—in fact, a wax doll. She escorts Dot and Tot through a series of enchanted valleys, the last of which is the Valley of Lost Things. It is a region to which lost objects ultimately find their way.

Baum doesn't explain how the objects get there, but I think I know. According to those philosophers called *panpsychics*, all objects possess, to some degree, a mind and consciousness. What we suppose are unique human traits fade back along the evolutionary continuum to micro-organisms, then extend—though in much lower degree—to such in-animate entities as stones, molecules, atoms, and particles.

"Even a potato in a dark cellar," wrote Samuel Butler, "has a certain low cunning...." And haven't you noticed that this is also true of rubber bands? When you stretch a band too tightly around something, and it breaks, does it not instantly disappear? If you find it, after a long search, is it not cleverly hiding in the most unlikely spot you can imagine? The elastic band is, of course, desperately trying to escape from this world. If you fail to find it, it lies there quietly in its secret spot for months, then one dark night it slips off through the fourth dimension to the Valley of Lost Things.

As you may know, I have mastered a technique that allows me to enter a trance during which my astral body can travel, not only to distant times and places, but also to imaginary worlds. It was on just such an OBE (out of body experience) that I visited the Valley of Lost Things.

Baum described the valley as devoid of life—nothing except enor-mous piles of such objects as pins, needles, thimbles, pennies, pencils, buttons, finger rings, overshoes, hats, gloves, handkerchiefs, and toys. I floated past other huge mounds of paperclips, match folders, umbrellas, chess and checker pieces, nuts and bolts, and one mammoth mound of lost playing cards. But Baum was wrong in thinking the valley uninhabited. Not far away was the Village of Lost Souls.

Judge Crater was mayor. Jimmy Hoffa was chief of police, Edwin Drood ran the town's sanitation department, and Amelia Earhart was the airport supervisor. I met dozens of other lost persons, but space is limited so I will speak only of my visit with the American writer of horror fantasy, Ambrose Bierce. Some of you will know that back in 1913 "Bitter Bierce," as he was called, made a trip to Mexico and was never heard of again. In *Wild Talents*, Charles Fort records that six years before Bierce vanished a man named Ambrose Small disappeared in Canada. "Was somebody collecting Ambroses?" Fort wanted to know.

Bierce enjoyed chess, and wrote a story called "Moxon's Master" about a chess machine that strangled its inventor when it lost a game. Bierce was also fond of puzzles. Indeed, he told me that his main hobby since he settled in the Village of Lost Souls was inventing puzzles that made use of the valley's endless supply of lost objects. He showed me many curious problems involving coins, toothpicks, paperclips, dice, dominoes, and so on, but his most memorable puzzle used five playing cards.

There were no cards in the small apartment Bierce shared with James Phillimore who, according to Dr. John Watson, stepped "back into his house to get his umbrella" and "was never more seen in this world." "I *must* show you this mathematical trick," said Bierce. "It will floor your readers. The Hill of Lost Cards is only a short tramp from here."

It was hard to keep up with Bierce's long strides. He was a tall muscular man, with white hair, pink skin, humorous gray-blue eyes, and a bushy yellow mustache. At the Hill of Lost Cards he rummaged about until he found five cards with identical backs.

"Doesn't matter what the faces are," he said, "so long as no two are alike and the backs the same. When you describe the trick, insist that your readers get five cards and follow the instructions carefully. The trick will destroy the cards, so tell them to look for an old deck with missing cards. Almost everybody has such a deck somewhere in the house. The missing cards have, of course, shuffled their way here to join their lost cousins."

I pause at this point. Dear reader, please get up now and go find five old cards you don't mind destroying. If you can't locate any, then draw the faces of five cards on file cards or paper rectangles. The rest of what I have to say will mean nothing unless you have the cards in hand. Believe me, it will be worth the effort. So go get the cards. Big Brother is watching!

Hold the five cards together and tear them in half as you would tear a single card.

Put one half on the other to make a packet of ten half-cards. "Cut" this packet as often as you like by making single cuts.

Divide the packet in half by sliding five cards to one side. Put the two packets on a table, face down and side by side. Turn the pile on the right face up.

You are now going to randomize the order of pieces in each pile by a spelling procedure that uses the last names of four famous writers of horror fantasy. The first word is LOVECRAFT. For the L, pick up either pile and transfer the top piece to the bottom. Replace the pile. For the O, again select either pile—it can be the one you used before, or the other one. Transfer the top piece to the bottom.

For the remaining seven letters, ... VECRAFT, repeat exactly the same procedure. For each letter, select whatever pile you like, then move the top piece to the bottom. After you finish spelling LOVECRAFT, remove the top piece of each pile, put one on the other (without turning over the face-down one) and set the pair aside.

Each pile now consists of four half-cards. The next word you spell is POE. As before, transfer a piece from top to bottom for each letter, always choosing a pile at random. When the spelling is finished, again remove the top piece of each pile and place the pair aside.

The piles have now diminished to three half-cards each. Spell BRADBURY. Put the two top pieces aside.

The piles now have two half-cards each. Spell BLOCH. Put aside the top pieces.

Two half-cards remain on the table, one face up, one face down. Because each word was spelled by taking a pile at random for each letter, it would be a weird coincidence, would it not, if those two remaining pieces matched? Turn over the face-down piece. If you followed these instructions properly, they will be the halves of the same card!

That's not all. The trick has a second climax that will blow your mind. Check the pairs you placed aside. Every pair will consist of matching halves!

Why does it always work? An explanation appears in the First Answers section.

6 AROUND THE SOLAR SYSTEM

In this chapter we examine a fantastic mathematical magic trick. I will present it as a puzzle—why does it always work?—but of course you can demonstrate it to friends as an amazing feat of ESP.

To the audience, this is how the trick appears. While your back is turned, someone is asked to put a dime on any of the nine squares shown on the facing page. Without turning around, you give instructions for moving the dime about at random over the matrix, as if it were a spaceship

6

touring the solar system. As these random moves are made, you keep blocking off certain cells by directing that pennies be placed on them. Finally, eight cells are occupied by pennies. With your back still turned, you can name the planet on which the "spaceship" came to rest.

Pause at this point and see that you have on hand a dime and eight pennies. Instead of pennies you can use buttons, checkers, or anything else that will serve as counters. I will now assume the role of magician while you assume the role of spectator.

Mercury	Uranus	Venus
Mars	Jupiter	Saturn
Neptune	Moon	Pluto

Select any one of the nine cells and put the dime on it. This is a completely free choice on your part, and obviously I have no way of knowing what choice you made. When you move the dime according to my instructions, you must move it one cell at a time in any horizontal or vertical direction. *No diagonal moves are allowed.* At each move you spell a letter in the name on the cell where you first put the dime. For example, if you start on Mars you spell M-A-R-S, moving the dime one square east, west, north, or south at random, one move for each letter.

When you finish spelling the name on the starting square, put a penny on Venus. I am, of course, betting that no matter where you began, or how you moved the dime, it will not have come to rest on Venus.

From now on, at each step of your "tour" of the solar system, you move the "spaceship" just seven times, regardless of the name on the cell. These moves are made randomly, as before, but are confined to unoccupied cells. The number of these vacant squares will become fewer and fewer as more and more pennies go on the matrix.

After making seven moves, put a penny on Mars.

Move seven times. Put a penny on Mercury. As New York City's mayor Ed Koch likes to say, "How'm I doin'?" Are all the pennies landing on vacant cells?

Move seven times. Put a penny on Uranus.

Move seven times. Put a penny on Neptune.

Move seven times. Put a penny on Saturn.

Move seven times. Put a penny on Jupiter.

Move seven times. Put a penny on the Moon.

If you followed instructions correctly, the dime should now be on Pluto!

When you show the trick to someone, turn your back while you give the above instructions. If you like, you can add to the mystery by allowing the spectator, at any time, to move by spelling S-E-V-E-N instead of counting seven. After he puts a penny on the moon, you can tell him, without turning around to look, that his dime is on Pluto.

Why does the trick always work? The answer will introduce you to the concept of "parity." It is a concept of enormous importance both in combinatorial mathematics and in modern particle physics; see the First Answers section.

7 THE STRIPE ON BARBERPOLIA

> Nothing moved...but the barbershop striped pole which turned slowly to show its red, white, and then red again, slid up out of nowhere to vanish nowhere, a motion between two mysteries.
>
> —Ray Bradbury, *I Sing the Body Electric*

The spaceship *Bagel* was on one of its long exploratory missions. "Good Lord!" a lookout shouted. "What am I seeing? I can't believe it!"

Lieutenant Flarp ambled over to look at the ship's forward telescope screen. On the monitor was what appeared to be a planet in the shape of a perfect right-circular cylinder!

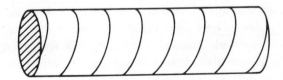

"It must be artificial," said Flarp. "There's no way a planet like that could form as a result of natural gravitational forces. Maybe it's a space station."

"Too big," said the lookout. "Voz [the ship's computer] gives the cylinder's length as 14,400 kilometers. That's longer than the earth's diameter."

"Ask Voz for the circumference."

Voz responded with 8,100 km.

When Flarp enlarged the image on the screen, his eyes bulged and his jaw sagged. Along the cylinder's smooth gray surface was a dark reddish stripe like the boundary lines on a barber's pole. Even more incredibly, the cylinder was rotating so rapidly that the helical stripe seemed to move along the cylinder.

"It certainly isn't a planet," said Flarp. "There's no atmosphere, and the damn thing is spinning so fast that centrifugal force would surely negate any gravity on the surface. I suppose it could be a hollow space station, rotating to generate an interior *g* field."

As the drawing shows, the helical stripe made exactly seven complete circuits around the cylinder's lateral surface.

The Bagel was soon speeding forward for a closer look, and possibly a landing on what the crew began to call Barberpolia. Your problem is: How long is the stripe?

You may think this a difficult question, but if you have the right *aha!* insight, it's ridiculously easy. Try to solve the problem before you look at the First Answers section.

8 THE ROAD TO MANDALAY

On the road to Mandalay,
Where the flyin' finches play.

During one of my out-of-body travels into the future, I found myself reincarnated in the body of a young man who was driving down a twenty-lane thruway. The road was jammed with cars and giant trucks, all rolling at speeds of about 200 km per hour. The sun had recently set, and here and there drivers were starting to turn on headlights. There was no danger of collisions because each vehicle was controlled by a powerful computer, aided by sophisticated sensory devices.

I had been driving since noon through Texas and Oklahoma, headed east for my home town of Mandalay. Mandalay? It's a drowsy little village of cotton farmers, 35 km southwest of Blytheville, Arkansas. I had finished my freshman year at the University of Arizona, planning to major in mathematics, and was on my way home for the summer.

The car I drove, named the Hustle, was made by robots in Hong Kong, and equipped with the most advanced talking computer on the international car market. To avoid motel bills I planned to drive all night. After a brief nap, while the car took over steering, I adjusted the dials on the computer console to give the Hustle access to its vast memory bank of logic and math problems.

"I'm in no mood for music," I said. "Would you mind tossing me some puzzles simple enough to work in my head?"

"You know I don't mind," said the car. "I'm programmed to do whatever you like—assuming, of course, I'm capable."

At that moment a flock of finches (sparrows) flew over the car, producing three white splotches on the windshield.

"How annoying," said the car. "But before I clean the windshield, observe that those three spots mark the corners of a triangle with sides close to the ratios of three, four, and five."

"By Euclid, you're right!"

"Which has the larger area? A triangle with sides of three, four, five, or a triangle with sides of 300, 400, and 700?"

"The second one, naturally."

"Wrong!" the car shot back, following its exclamation with an infuriating metallic chuckle. "The second triangle is degenerate. It's a straight line. Its area is *zero*."

"Okay, okay, pal," I said. "I didn't stop to think. Let's have another one. And please—no cackling if I miss."

I was able to solve most of the car's brain teasers. Here are some I either couldn't crack or I answered incorrectly. Maybe you can do better. The questions should be answered without using pencil, paper, or calculator—and remember, the car's a hustler.

1. "Take a look at my digital clock," said the car. "It shows eight o'clock. How many 5's will appear as numerals on the clock between now and nine?"

2. "How many times, between noon and midnight, will the clock show at least three digits that are alike? They don't have to be adjacent."

3. "Suppose you have to stop and change a flat," said the car. "As you know, each of my wheels has four nuts. You put the nuts on the ground. While you're unlocking the spare, a squirrel steals all four nuts. What's the best way to get me safely to the nearest garage?"

4. "For 10,000 km, assume you rotate my tires so I make equal use of all five. How many kilometers of wear does each tire suffer?"

5. "Suppose you and a friend in another car started on this trip at the same time in Tucson. He never exceeds the speed limit, and we never get ahead of him for the entire trip. Could we get ticketed for (and be guilty of) speeding?"

6. When we passed a farm with a square fence around it, the car asked a question that seemed so easy I wanted to kick myself for flubbing it. "If the farm has a perimeter of 400 meters, 100 on each side, and the farmer put up a fence post every ten meters, how many posts did he use?"

7. After paying at a toll bridge, the car asked: "What's the largest sum, made up of U.S. coins, that will not change a dollar bill, and how can

this sum be given by the largest number of coins so that these coins still cannot change one dollar?" I guessed $1.19, using eleven coins—three quarters, four dimes, and four pennies.

8. "And you plan to be a mathematician?" said the car. "Maybe you can do better on this one. What's the *smallest* number of coins that *will* change a dollar bill if you obey the rule that no coin of the same value can be used an even number of times. For example, you can't use two halves or four quarters."

For answers to these questions, see the First Answers section.

9 THE BLACK HOLE OF CAL CUTTER

Calvin Cutter, or "Calcutta" as some friends call him, is a collector and maker of paradoxes. I don't mean paradoxes of the sort that can be written down, but physical objects that seem impossible.

When I visited Cal in the spring of 2085, he had moved his fantastic collection into a small building behind his house. One room was filled entirely with topological curiosities. There were large glass models of Klein bottles and projective planes, closed surfaces with no outside or inside. A huge piece of steel looked like two Moebius bands, one nested inside the other. You could run your fingers around the loop, between the bands to prove they were separate, yet it was only a single band that looped around twice. Two large wooden rings, each made of a different wood, were linked together. Careful inspection showed that neither ring had been cut in any way.

"How in thunder did you construct this?" I asked.

"I usually don't explain," said Cal, "but in your case I'll make an exception. When I was a small boy I cut a notch in a young pine tree growing in the woods near where I lived. I shoved a mahogany torus into the notch. Thirty years later, after the tree had grown around and through the torus, I sawed out a portion of the tree and whittled the second ring. Then I stained and polished the wood. Aren't they beautiful?"

"Our friend Cecil Wyche," I said, "tells me he sent you details about a paradoxical hole he invented, and you actually made one. Is that true?"

"It is indeed," said Cal. "The hole gets smaller and smaller as you go down, tapering off into such a fine filament that I have the hole buried in the yard to protect its delicate lower end. Come—I'll show you."

Cutter led me to a spot behind his museum where a protective fence surrounded what looked like an enormous cubical hole. The sides were made of metal and painted black. A sign on the gate read: "The Black Hole of Calcutta."

"Ten years ago it would have been impossible to construct this monstrosity," said Cal. "But as you know, it was in 2076 that the great Chinese physicist No Lim Sum revolutionized quantum mechanics by his discovery that matter consists of an infinite hierarchy of smaller and smaller particles."

I nodded. "Like a nest of Chinese boxes. The sequence never ends. There *is* no smallest particle."

"Precisely. And it was only a few years later that chemists at the Livermore Laboratory developed techniques for making compounds with subquark particles that could be made as small as one pleased."

I must pause at this point to describe Cutter's black hole. It consisted of an infinite sequence of cubical sides that became progressively smaller. Think of the hole (the top portion of which is shown in the figure) as made up of cubes without tops or bottoms.

The largest cube was exactly one decameter (about 33 feet) along an edge. Directly beneath were the sides of a cube with an edge of $1/\sqrt{2}$, or close to .7 dm. The third cube was $1/\sqrt{3}$ on the side, or about .57 dm. The side of the fourth cube, $1/\sqrt{4}$, was exactly .5 dm, and so on for an infinity of smaller and smaller cubes. Letting n be the cube's position from the top, each cube had a side of $1/\sqrt{n}$.

We can write the series of edge lengths like this:

$$\frac{1}{\sqrt{1}} + \frac{1}{\sqrt{2}} + \frac{1}{\sqrt{3}} + \frac{1}{\sqrt{4}} + \cdots + \frac{1}{\sqrt{n}}.$$

9

Because the volume of the n-th cube is $1/\sqrt{n} \times 1/\sqrt{n} \times 1/\sqrt{n}$, the series of volumes can be written:

$$\frac{1}{1\sqrt{1}} + \frac{1}{2\sqrt{2}} + \frac{1}{3\sqrt{3}} + \frac{1}{4\sqrt{4}} + \cdots + \frac{1}{n\sqrt{n}}.$$

The above sequence, Cal explained, converges. This means that its sum is a finite number. I don't know the exact sum, but it is less than 3 cubic dm.

"It was easy to paint the hole's interior," said Cal. "I just filled the hole with black paint. Of course I had to use a special paint made of infinitely small molecules. Otherwise, a molecule of finite size would have

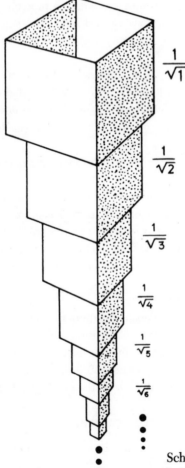

Schematic diagram of Cal Cutter's hole

clogged the hole when it became smaller than a molecule. Then I pumped out all the paint, which left the hole painted black, as you see."

"I can understand all that," I said, "but where's the paradox?"

Cal smiled enigmatically. "The paradox rears its frightening head when you calculate the painted area. Let's go inside and I'll show you the simple mathematics."

Cal was right. When we finished calculating the interior surface area of the hole, it almost blew my mind. Try to determine it before looking at the First Answers section.

10 SCIENCE FANTASY QUIZ

Here are nine short problems with science fiction angles. A few call for some knowledge of physics, but most are easily solved if you have the right burst of insight.

1. On what planet can you throw a rock in such a way that it goes a short distance, stops in midair, reverses direction, and travels back to you. No, it doesn't bounce off anything.

2. An astronaut exploring the Moon bet his companion that with his eyes tightly closed he could walk a distance of exactly one kilometer. How did he win the bet?

3. Which came first, the chicken or the egg?

4. In Lord Dunsany's *Fourth Book of Jorkens*, Jorkens insists that six months earlier he had made a trip through space to a spot in the solar system, on the other side of the sun, opposite where the Earth is now. A skeptical member of the Billiards Club bets him five pounds he can't prove it. How does Jorkens win the bet?

5. Is there a structure on the Earth, made by human hands, that can be seen with unaided eyes from the Moon?

6. In Ross Tocklynne's SF yarn, "At the Center of Gravity," some men are trapped at the center of a hollow sphere as large as the Earth. The force of gravity has drawn them there. In Wells's *First Men in the Moon*, gravity pulls Wells's space travelers to the center of their spherical ship. What's wrong here?

7. Imagine an enormous gyroscope constructed on the equator. As the Earth turns, the axis of the gyroscope will keep its orientation relative to the stars. Relative to the Earth, however, the axis will make a complete

rotation every 24 hours. Would this not be a form of perpetual motion, allowing useful energy to be taken from the rotating gyroscope?

8. Below are the numbers 1, 2, 3, and zero, with the 1 horizontal as it is often written in Japan. What well known magazine that publishes science fiction is represented by the digits below?

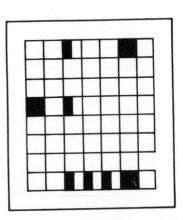

9. Diagrams can be sent easily over interstellar distances by a binary pulsed code that indicates which cells in a rectangular matrix are to be darkened. What message is conveyed by the matrix shown above?

11 THE BARBERS OF BARBERPOLIA

In Chapter 7 we left the crew of the spaceship *Bagel* wondering why a dark red stripe spiraled around a cylindrical planet they had encountered. The crew had named the mysterious planet *Barberpolia* because it rotated like a barber's pole.

After the Bagel's home base granted permission to explore the cylindrical object, Captain Larc Snaag, and his exobiologist Stanley Winetree, took off in a small shuttle ship. They circled the planet warily. At the center of one of its ends was what appeared to be a large entrance in the metallic surface.

When the ship landed, three humanoids in space suits emerged from the opening and gave what seemed to be friendly greetings. Snaag and Winetree were escorted inside.

Sensory devices on Winetree's belt transmitted data about the cylinder's atmosphere to VOZ, the Bagel's supercomputer. The air was similar to that on Earth, VOZ relayed back, and could be breathed with safety. Snaag, Winetree, and the three Barberpolians took off their helmets.

The faces of the natives were entirely covered with short reddish hair. Otherwise they looked remarkably human except for their smaller eyes, flatter noses, and wider mouths. Snaag and Winetree could hardly believe their ears when one of the natives called out, in curiously accented but recognizable English, "Welcome, men of Earth, to our planet!"

For several weeks Snaag and Winetree were lavishly entertained. The cylindrical planet, which rotated to generate a gravity field, had been constructed by a culture with a technology on roughly the same level as Earth's. The natives had formerly occupied a planet in another part of the universe, but when nuclear warfare had rendered the surface uninhabitable, the survivors found it necessary to build the artificial planet. It was in orbit around a small black hole which was used both as a source of energy and for waste disposal. The helical stripe? It was an enormous tube that carried atmosphere from huge machines at the ends of the cylinder to all parts of the planet.

A century before the cylinder was built, a group of Barberpolians had visited the Earth. They came, they told Snaag and Winetree, in dish-like ships. Apparently those ships had been responsible for the UFO mania that swept the Earth in the latter part of the twentieth century.

"We were extremely careful to avoid all interactions with humans," said one of the Barberpolians who had learned English, "but after several

decades of observations we mastered the English language well enough to read the many books we were able to steal, and to understand our recordings of your conversations. Your rotating barber poles intrigued us because hair cutting and washing is a major aspect of our lives. When we found it necessary to twist the air tube around our planet, we colored it red so that when the cylinder rotated it would resemble one of your beautiful barber poles."

"I've noticed," said Snaag, "many such poles rotating outside little shops on your streets. Are those barbershops?"

"They are indeed," said the native. "We have thousands in every city. As you can see, our entire body from head to toes is covered with thick hair. We evolved on a planet colder than yours, and our protective hair grows much faster than the hair on your heads. In the controlled and warmer climate of our new planet, we need to have our hair constantly trimmed and shampooed."

When Snaag and Winetree visited a barbershop they were amazed by how rapidly and skillfully the barbers worked. The natives wore no clothing of any sort, but their hair covered them so completely that the only way to recognize a female was by a small bald spot on top of her head.

All barbers were female. Sometimes they helped each other when the shop was crowded. Using electrical clippers, a barber could trim a customer's entire body in ten minutes. A shampoo took five minutes.

Assume that three Barberpolian men, A, B, and C enter a shop at the same time. Each wants a trim and a shampoo. Only two barbers are on duty. A shampoo must be completed in one unbroken time period of five minutes, and given by a single barber. Two barbers are not allowed to work on a customer at the same time, although one barber may start a trim and another finish it, with a time lapse in between. It does not matter whether a trim follows a shampoo or vice versa.

How quickly can two barbers give the three men their haircuts and shampoos? See the First Answers section.

12 IT'S ALL DONE WITH MIRRORS

> Mirrors have something monstrous about them.
> —Jorge Luis Borges, "Tlön, Uqbar, Orbis Tertius,"

After the spaceship *Bagel* left Barberpolia, Captain Larc Snaag ordered a shift to the Bagel's inertial hyperdrive. Several days went by uneventfully as the Bagel sped through the Milky Way Galaxy at almost the velocity of light. Suddenly the giant ship slammed into a totally unanticipated space warp created by a wandering black hole.

The ship's lighting system momentarily failed. Furniture and other objects were tossed about, crew members began to scream, and for several minutes the *Bagel* seemed to be tumbling like a child doing somersaults. A better metaphor: it was as if some monstrous creature had picked up the ship and flipped it the way one flips a coin. Then just as abruptly everything was calm, and the ship was moving smoothly on its original course.

Lieutenant Flarp, the officer on duty in the control room, reported at once to Captain Snaag.

"We don't know yet what happened," he said, his face still ashen, "but there has been some minor damage to the propulsion system. The engineering department tells me it will be difficult to make repairs while the ship is moving. They request a landing."

Snaag had just picked himself up from the floor, and was still feeling parts of his anatomy. No bones had been broken, though there were some painful bruises. "We'll land on the first suitable planet," he said. "I'll be along soon to take over the controls."

The *Bagel* was passing through an uncharted region of the galaxy, but by a stroke of good fortune, the radar screen spotted a planet only slightly larger than Earth. Careful analysis of the laser probes, by the ship's supercomputer VOZ, indicated no lifeforms on the planet. There also was no atmosphere, but because the repairs could be made from inside, this created no problem.

The *Bagel* made an easy landing. While the repairs were underway, Flarp washed his face and stuck a bandage over a small cut above his left eye. He was combing his hair in front of the mirror when suddenly a bizarre thought struck him.

"According to VOZ," he said to himself, "the *Bagel* flipped over several times when it plowed through five-dimensional spacetime. That means it must have rotated outside our three-space. Great Asimov! If we flipped over an odd number of times, then our ship and everything in it has been mirror reflected. That cut is really over my right eye, the way it looks in this mirror."

Flarp opened his medicine cabinet. The printing on the jars looked normal. "How idiotic of me," he thought, slapping his forehead on the unwounded side. "Of course the print would read the same even if we are reversed. My entire head, eyes and brain included, would have exchanged left and right sides. If the printing is reversed, it would still look normal."

Flarp frowned and massaged his cheek. "I must see what VOZ has to say."

VOZ listened attentively while Flarp asked him how many times the ship had turned over in four-space. "Sorry," he replied, "but I have no data. All the circuits blanked out, including mine, when we went through the warp."

"It must be possible, then," said Flarp, "that all of us are now mirror images of our former selves. If you took an asymmetric Flatlander out of his plane, turned him over an odd number of times in three-space, then returned him to his planiverse, he would be mirror reversed. It's the same . . . ."

"You don't have to explain," VOZ interrupted. "I understand perfectly. You forget that I'm programmed to visualize in higher dimensions. But don't worry. We're not reversed. We had a narrow escape, though. Someone should have consulted me before we landed for repairs."

How could VOZ be so certain that the *Bagel* had flipped over an even number of times? And why had he been so concerned about the landing? [See the First Answers section.]

13 SATAN AND THE APPLE

I had occasion recently to spend a few weeks in San Francisco. Early one afternoon, while I was finishing lunch at the Caffe Puccini in the North Beach section—it's a spot where some of my more eccentric Silicon Valley friends hang out—an attractive young woman with red hair came over to the booth where I was sitting alone.

"Are you Martin Gardner?" she asked.

"That's me," I replied, putting aside the newspaper I had been reading.

"May I sit down?"

"Of course."

A mutual friend, she said, had told her I would be there. She was a subscriber to *Isaac Asimov's Science Fiction Magazine*, and she read my puzzle column every month. There was a strange story she wanted to tell me. She was sure I could make use of it in my column.

"It all started three years ago," she said, "a few weeks after I got my Ph.D., in astrophysics at Stanford. My thesis was on the latest models of the inflationary universe—you know, the universe that starts with a big bang, then instantly inflates, and . . ."

"You don't have to explain," I interrupted. "I know about the models."

"Well," she continued, "I was sitting at the console of my Apple computer one night—it was late, about three in the morning—when I started to doze. I let my fingers wander idly over the keys . . ."

"Were you weary and ill at ease?" I asked. "Like the lady at the organ when she found that lost chord?"

"Exactly," she said. "That's how it was. I can't remember what I was thinking or dreaming about, but suddenly there was a loud explosion. The room filled with smoke. It smelled terrible. When the smoke cleared, there was Satan leering at me."

I couldn't help grinning. "What did the old fellow look like?"

"Just like his pictures," she said. "He was tall and handsome, wearing red tights, and he had a black mustache and pointed beard. There were two little horns on his head, and a long forked tail at his rear. He told me my fingers had hit on an old cabalistic combination of numbers and letters that forced him to appear. He offered me anything I desired."

"Of course you refused."

"No," she said. "I was too anxious to learn how the cosmos began. My thesis analyzed all the latest big bang models, but naturally I didn't know which was true. Maybe they were all false. I wanted to know what really happened back there in time some fifteen or twenty billion years ago."

"Did he tell you?"

"He did. And I must say his answer floored me. Maybe I shouldn't have been so surprised. After all, if it wasn't for the Bible we wouldn't know Satan existed. Right?"

"Right," I said, "What the devil did he tell you?"

"He told me the universe was formed just like it says in Genesis. Jehovah created everything out of nothing in six days, each twenty-four hours long. Then he rested on the seventh."

"If that's the case," said I, "the universe must be only six to ten thousand years old. What about the stars so far away that the light we see from them must have started millions of years ago?"

"I asked Satan about that," she said. "He told me the universe was created with all that light already on the way."

"And the fossils?"

"They're the records of plants and animals that were wiped out by Noah's flood."

"Are you trying to tell me," I said, "that the fundamentalists are right? That evolution is a false theory, and everything happened in six literal days just the way the Old Testament has it?"

"Yes," she said sadly. "That's what I learned from Satan. And he ought to know. He was there when it happened."

I studied her face carefully. It was a pretty face, with intelligent, unshifty eyes that looked directly into mine and betrayed not the slightest trace of insincerity. A sudden thought popped into my head.

"Satan," I said, "has a reputation of never giving anything away free. There's always a bargain. You must have offered him something. What did you give in exchange for this information?"

She smiled faintly, looked nervously around the room, then bent over and whispered. "I gave up the ability of ever telling the truth when I meet someone for the first time." [See the First Answers section for some commentary.]

---

14 HOW'S-THAT-AGAIN FLANAGAN

I've known a number of top science fiction writers in my day, but none whose conversation was more bewildering than that of Fred Flanagan. You won't recognize his name because Fred writes under a dozen pseudonyms. His novels and stories are noted for their wild cosmologies and their bizarre planets. He acquired the unusual nickname of How's-That-Again, or Howse for short, when he was a student at the Bronx High School of Science. The name reflected his habit of perpetually making such curious, outlandish remarks that listeners frequently responded with "How's that again?"

A few months ago I visited Flanagan at what he called the "Howse house" on the shore of Paradox Lake, a small lake in Essex County, New York, about six miles west of the upper Hudson River. Although only in his mid-forties, Fred had grown a long beard that he bleached white to make him look like a Zen sage. To avoid the nuisance of washing his hair and having it cut he shaved his head every few days.

"Those jeans you're wearing," I said, pointing to his feet, "are awfully narrow at the bottoms. How do you manage to get your feet through them?"

"I don't," he said, "I put 'em on over my head."

I should explain that Fred had inherited from his Irish immigrant parents a fondness for Irish bulls. I once asked him why he and his ex-wife never had any children. "Sterility," he replied. "My wife was unable to conceive. She inherited the disability from her mother."

"How's that again?" I remember asking.

We were paddling about Paradox Lake in Flanagan's canoe when I brought up the Kaluza-Klein theory, a strange conjecture that I discussed at some length in my *Ambidextrous Universe*. I call it strange because it posits a fourth spatial dimension that curves back on itself like a circle, but with a diameter much shorter than the radius of an atom! Einstein had rejected the theory, and I never expected it would ever be revived. To my vast surprise, a generalized Kaluza-Klein theory, with more spatial dimensions than four, is now a hot topic in the latest GUTs (Grand Unification Theories) that are attempting to unify all the forces of nature and to explain the quantum properties of all the fundamental particles.

"I'm not surprised at all," said Flanagan. "Spacetime has to be at least five-dimensional because it's easy to show that a cube has four space dimensions."

"How's that again?"

"Consider a square," Fred said. "Its two diagonals are perpendicular to each other. This proves a square is two-dimensional. Now take a cube. It has four space diagonals, each joining opposite pairs of corners. As you can easily see, any two space diagonals are perpendicular to one another. Of course four mutually perpendicular lines can be drawn only in four-dimensional space."

I was about to make a comment, but Flanagan interrupted. "Do you know what a naked singularity is?"

I nodded. "Some cosmologists think a collapsing star can form something much worse than a black hole. It's a singularity in spacetime that is 'unclothed,' so to speak, by a black hole. Light can spiral around it and escape."

"Precisely," Fred said. "A Cambridge cosmologist named George Ellis has based a marvelous model of the universe on a naked singularity.

He assumes that the universe is the surface of a vast four-dimensional sphere, like some early models, only the sphere is not expanding."

"Then how does Ellis explain the red shift?" I asked. "As you know, it's the shifting of the spectrum of distant stars toward the red that is the strongest evidence for an expanding universe."

"Nonsense," said Flanagan. "There are dozens of ways to explain the red shift. Ellis accounts for it this way. Our Milky Way galaxy is at a spot on the hypersphere's surface exactly opposite a monstrous naked singularity. The monster pulls into itself all the matter that is spewing out from exploding supernovae and other cosmic events. It transforms this matter into hydrogen, which it spews out again. This recycling of matter keeps the cosmos in a steady state."

"And the red shift?"

"I'm coming to that. The more distant a galaxy is from us the closer it is to the naked singularity. The intense gravity field around the singularity shifts starlight toward the red. The closer a star is to the monster, the greater the shift. For observers on earth this creates the illusion of an expanding universe. If we could look at our galaxy from a planet nearer the singularity we would see the light blue-shifted."

"Wouldn't it be an unbelievable coincidence that our galaxy and the singularity are antipodal?"

"Not at all," said Flanagan. "Only a galaxy that far from the singularity would be cool enough to allow life to evolve. We're here because we couldn't have evolved anywhere else."

"And you take all this seriously?"

"It's the best model we have. Of course it has one great weakness. It assumes that gravity is an attractive force."

"How's that again?"

"Haven't you ever wondered why a gas-filled balloon rises?"

"It's gravity pulling the air down and creating pressure on the underside."

"But that's absurd," said Flanagan. "There's just as much air pressure pushing down on the top of the balloon. There may be a slight difference between the pressure above and below, but this is much too small to make a balloon rise as fast as it does. No, the balloon is pushed up by gravity."

"But if gravity pushes it up," I said, "what makes a stone fall?"

"It's the enormous pressure of all the countless billions upon billions of virtual particles that keep bubbling up in the quantum foam of the so-called vacuum of space."

I decided to change the subject. "Are there any fish in this lake?"

"Plenty," said Fred. "But I never fish. I hate fishing, and what's more, I'm glad I hate it."

"How come?"

"Because," he said, "if I liked to fish I'd be spending lots of time fishing, and that would bore me to death. One of my neighbors loves to fish. Unfortunately, he lost his left arm in an auto accident many years ago so he has to fish with one hand. The other day he told me he caught a fish so big..."

Flanagan put his left arm behind his back to imitate a one-armed man. Then he extended his right hand, palm to the left, to show how big the fish was.

"By the way," he said, "this canoe reminds me of a clever word problem your readers might enjoy. Ask them if they can rearrange the letters of CANOE to make another common English word."

A few days after I returned home I received a postcard from Flanagan. On the address side was pasted a small sticker that said: "Please notify the post office immediately if this sticker has fallen off in transit." On the back of the card was typed:

Don't waste your time reading this. It doesn't say anything.

It should be easy to figure out the flimflam about the cube, to explain why balloons rise, and to find an anagram for CANOE. See First Answers section. As for George Ellis, he really is a distinguished British cosmologist whose model has been put forth seriously. You can find out more about it in Paul Davies's 1981 book *The Edge of Infinity.*

15 RELATIVISTICALLY SPEAKING

"The Captain tells me you're having trouble with relativity theory," said Lieutenant Flarp to Ensign Pulver. The two officers were chatting over cups of coffee in the cafeteria of the spaceship Bagel.

"You hear right," sighed Pulver. "The Old Man says he won't recommend my advancement in rank until I pass my test on the special theory of relativity."

"Any particular problems? Maybe I can help."

Pulver put down his cup and opened a new pack of Marsborough cigarettes. Made from choice tobacco cultivated on Mars, they came in bright red packages of 50 thin cigarettes to a box. "I keep thinking of situations I can't understand. It seems to me they violate the theory."

"Such as?"

"Well, suppose I'm standing on a planet and two spaceships go by directly overhead in opposite directions. Each ship is moving, say, at three-fourths the speed of light. Won't they pass each other with one-and-one-half times the speed of light?"

"They will."

"But doesn't relativity theory say that no object can pass another with a speed faster than light?"

"It does indeed," said Flarp, "but that applies only to observers on the objects. From your fixed frame of reference on the planet you'd see the ships go past each other with relative speeds greater than light. But if you're on one of the ships it's a different story. You'd have to consider the changes in length and time that occur when relative speeds are high."

"Is there a formula for that?"

"There is," said Flarp, "and a very simple one. In Newtonian physics you would of course merely add the velocities of the two ships. But in relativity theory velocities are not additive. If one ship goes in one direction with velocity x and the other goes the opposite way with velocity y, the passing speed for an observer on either ship isn't x plus y. It's x plus y divided by 1 plus xy over c squared, where c is the speed of light."

Pulver put down his box of cigarettes and inked the following formula on a paper napkin:

$$\frac{x + y}{1 + \dfrac{xy}{c^2}}.$$

[For a detailed discussion of relativistic velocities, see *The Role of Mathematics in Science* by M. M. Schiffer and L. Bowden, New Mathematical Library volume 30 (1984), Mathematical Association of America.]

For x he substituted $3c/4$ (three fourths the speed of light), and the same for y. It took only a few minutes to see that when the formula is reduced, c^2 cancels out giving $24c/25$ or $24/25$ths the speed of light for the passing velocity of the two ships.

"Beautiful!" exclaimed Pulver. "I had no idea the calculation was so easy. Let me ask you something else. Imagine an enormous pair of scissors in space. Its blades are as long as the diameter of the solar system. Now suppose the blades slowly start to close. The spot where their cutting edges intersect will move toward the points of the scissors with a speed that keeps getting faster. Wouldn't the velocity of that crossing point, relative to me, soon exceed that of light?"

"It would," said Flarp. "But I'm sure you realize that only a geometrical point is moving, not a material object. Relativity theory allows all sorts of things to go faster than light. You can move a beam of light inside a dark room and make the spot on the wall go faster than light."

"I understand that," said Pulver, "but what troubles me is this. Suppose the handles of the scissors are on earth and the spot where the edges cross is at Pluto. Couldn't we wiggle the handles to make the intersection point jiggle back and forth, and send a coded message to Pluto that would travel faster than light? I may be wrong, but doesn't relativity theory absolutely prohibit sending messages at speeds faster than light?"

"It certainly does," said Flarp. He then proceeded to explain why the giant scissors couldn't be used for faster-than-light signaling. If you have trouble figuring it out, turn to the next answers section.

16 BAR BETS ON THE BAGEL

Ensign Pulver, Lieutenant Flarp, and Colonel Couth were relaxing in the bar of the spaceship *Bagel*. Pulver, who had a passion for curious tricks and puzzles, especially puzzles with a catch answer, picked up a folder of matches.

"You may not believe it," he said, pointing to a glass of water on the table, "but I can light a match and cause it to burn under the water in that glass."

Flarp groaned. "Okay, Pulver. I don't believe it. Let's see you do it."

Flarp struck a match. Then he picked up the glass of water and held the burning match below it.

Flarp groaned again, but louder.

Pulver tore another match out of the folder. "Here's another good one. I'll bet you can't drop this match on the table, from a height of a meter, and make it land so it stands on an edge."

"I know that one," said Couth. He picked up the match, bent it into the shape of a V, and dropped it.

Pulver seemed not in the least dismayed. From his pocket he took a small coin, about the size of what was called a dime in the United States back in the twentieth century. "How about this? Drop the coin from a height of six centimeters so it lands on the table and stays upright on its edge."

Flarp and Couth thought about this while they sipped their crimson-colored Martian martinis. When they gave up, Pulver dipped the coin in the glass of water, pressed it against the outside of the glass near the rim, then let go. The water made the coin adhere to the straight side of the glass. The coin slid to the table and remained on its edge, still clinging to the glass.

This time both Flarp and Couth groaned.

"Now it's my turn to show *you* one," said Couth to Pulver. He arranged four matches on the table to form a martini glass. Then he picked the cholive out of his cocktail and placed it inside the glass as shown below, left. (Cholives are tiny brown berries obtained by crossing olive and cherry trees. The hybrid trees were first cultivated on Mars, where their fruit quickly became a popular ingredient of most Martian cocktails.)

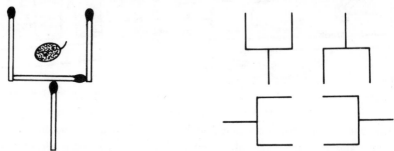

"What's the problem?" asked Pulver.

"Very simple," Couth replied. "You are to pick up just two matches, then replace them so as to form a new martini glass, but with the cholive *outside* the glass. The glass must be like the one you started with except it needn't have the same orientation."

"I assume I'm not allowed to touch the cholive."

"You assume right," said Couth. "Otherwise you could simply move the cholive outside without moving *any* matches."

Let me restate the problem to make it clear. Move just two matches to make a martini glass, of the same size and shape as the original, but with the cholive on the outside. The reformed glass may be in any of the four orientations shown in the figure above, right.

It's a great puzzle to show friends. You'll be surprised how difficult it is, though if you have the right insight you may solve it quickly, before looking at the First Answers Section.

17 CATCH THE BEM

On the planet Evenod the most popular household pet is a small BEM (bug-eyed monster) with a personality somewhat like that of an earth dog, though less docile. You see, below, the streets of a town on Evenod. An Evenoder, at the street intersection indicated by the letter E, is trying to catch his runaway pet BEM at an intersection southeast of him.

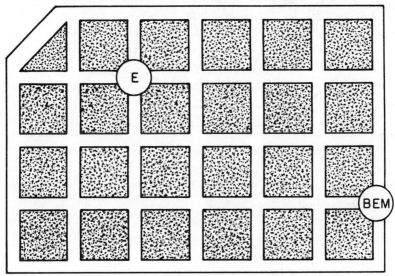

Put a penny on spot E and a dime on the BEM spot. You now have an amusing game to play with a friend. Here are the simple rules:

1. Players alternate turns, one moving the penny, the other moving the dime. The Evenoder (penny) always goes first.

2. Each move is one block in any direction.

3. The Evenoder catches the BEM by moving his penny on top of the dime.

4. The Evenoder wins if he catches the BEM in 50 or fewer of his own moves. The BEM wins if he is not caught by this time.

After playing the game for a while you will discover that the BEM is not easy to catch. It seems impossible to trap the beast in a corner. However, there is a secret strategy that enables the Evenoder to trap his pet quickly. See the First Answers section.

Where, on Evenod, did the BEM go?

18 ANIMAL TTT

If you don't know about polyominoes, you are missing one of the most intriguing fields of modern recreational mathematics. Arthur Clarke became so fascinated by them that he put them into his novel *Imperial Earth* as symbols of the combinatorial possibilities of life. In his recent book *Ascent to Orbit* you'll find a chapter titled "Help! I Am a Pentomino Addict!" Remember the chess game played by HAL, the computer in Clarke's film *2001*? This was first filmed as a pentomino game, but for various reasons was later changed to chess.

Pentominoes are a species of polyomino. A polyomino? It is a structure made of unit squares joined along their sides. A single square is called a monomino. Two make a domino. Three join in two different ways to make two trominoes. Four join to make five tetrominoes, and there are twelve different pentominoes of five squares each. The terminology was invented by Professor S. W. Golomb, of the University of Southern California, who was the first to study polyominoes in depth. He has written an entire book titled *Polyominoes* (1965), unfortunately no longer in print.

Is there a formula that gives at once the number of different n-ominoes for every n? Probably not; this is one of the most intractable problems in combinatorial geometry. The best computer algorithms for enumerating all the polyominoes for a given n are recursive—they first determine all the polyominoes for $n - 1$ before they go on to n. No one has yet discovered a way of determining the number of different n-ominoes in a less laborious way.

Frank Harary, a graph theorist at the University of Michigan, likes to think of polyominoes as *n*-celled "animals." Most polyomino problems involve forming patterns with a given set of animals, but in the past few years Harary has invented a bewildering variety of simple games with these animals that are great fun to play. Some of the games raise deep combinatorial questions not yet answered.

The games are played on paper like ticktactoe (TTT). The basic idea is for two players to take turns marking the cells of a square matrix with zeros and crosses, but instead of trying to get three of their marks in a row, they try to form a specified animal or its mirror image. Each game has its reverse form—Harary calls it an avoidance game—in which the first to form the animal *loses*. Avoidance games are usually much harder to analyze.

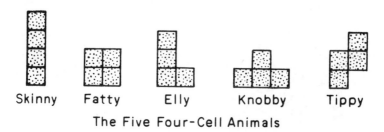

Skinny   Fatty   Elly   Knobby   Tippy
The Five Four-Cell Animals

For example, assume that the game's animal is what Harary calls Tippy (see above), and that the game is played on an order-3 (three-by-three) square field. The first player to form Tippy, in either of its mirror-image forms, wins. When I first published this game in *Scientific American* in 1979, both Harary and I considered it a draw if both sides played rationally (their best), but Terence Martin, then a student of Harary at Ann Arbor, found a simple strategy by which the first player can always win.

You'll enjoy playing Tippy TTT with friends. See if you can discover the winning first-player strategy. It is given in the First Answers section.

19 PLAYING SAFE ON THE BAGEL

Every officer on the spaceship *USS Bagel* has a private safe in which to keep valuables. The figure on p. 41 shows the pattern of pushbuttons on each safe. An officer chooses a triplet of three letters, then sets the lock so it opens only when the three letters are pushed in the right order.

Duplicate letters are allowed, so the number of possible triples is $26 \times 26 \times 26 = 17,576$. Pushing the one-dot button opens the safe. The button with two dots locks it. Officers may alter their triplet whenever they wish.

Tanya, the teen-age daughter of Colonel Couth, head of the ship's computer science division, had been reading a biography of the great twentieth-century physicist Richard Feynman. As a young man in Los Alamos, where scientists worked on the first atomic bombs, Feynman became skillful at guessing the numerical keys that his fellow-workers selected for their office safes. He liked to leave in their safes little notes warning them of the need for tighter security.

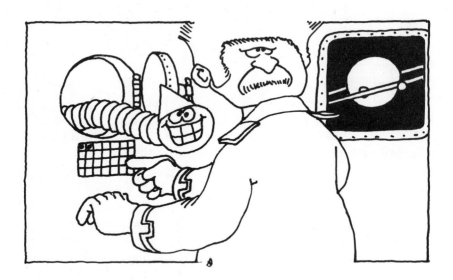

Tanya was soon amusing herself and annoying officers by doing the same thing on the *Bagel*. The officers had a habit of selecting three-letter words that were easily memorized, and that had a special significance for them. VOZ, the name of the ship's computer, was a popular word. (It is obtained from HAL, Arthur Clarke's famous spaceship computer, by shifting each letter 14 steps forward in the alphabet.) Ensign Pulver was enormously fond of science fiction by the Polish writer Stanislaw Lem. Tanya sneaked into his room one day and, sure enough, LEM opened his safe. Shift each letter of LEM forward 14 steps and you get ZSA, a popular word among crew members who were ancient-movie buffs.

Tanya drew up a list of unusual three-letter words such as PYX, CWM, PSI, GRR, TCH, PST, and acronyms like IBM, USA, RBI, and so on. It took only a few minutes to run rapidly down the list to see if any of the words opened a safe.

20

"You've done us all a service," Couth said to his daughter. "Security on the ship is much stronger since you began guessing everybody's secret word. Officers are now starting to randomize their triplets."

"Did you randomize your latest key?" Tanya asked.

"No. I selected a common mathematical word. It uses only letters on the grey keys."

Tanya walked over to the wall safe and studied the buttons. "But how can that be? All the vowels are on white. Even Y is white."

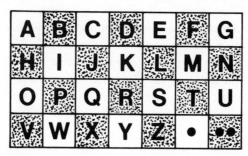

"I know," said Couth. "It's really an astonishing coincidence that A, E, I, O, U, and Y are all at odd-numbered positions in the alphabet. Nevertheless, there *is* a common three-letter word—you hear me use it constantly—with all its letters on gray buttons."

Can you guess the word? It is given in the First Answers section.

20 SEX AMONG THE POLYOMANS

You may recall that in the first chapter I reported a revolutionary discovery by Japan's top geneticist Dr. Mitsu Matsu. Using new techniques of genetic engineering Dr. Matsu was able to construct microorganisms that are virtually two-dimensional and are capable of living and breeding in monolayer liquid films, that is, in films only one molecule thick. They inhabit that curious borderland between nonliving crystals and organic life forms. I discussed a large genus of Dr. Matsu's microorganisms that he calls rep-tiles because they reproduce by splitting into four smaller copies of themselves.

Since that report, Dr. Matsu has continued his sensational research. Early this year he succeeded in fabricating monolayer organisms in the shapes of flat polyominoes, a type of polygon that was discussed in Chapter 18. A polyomino is easily defined. It is a polygon produced by fitting identical unit squares together at their edges.

20

Dr. Matsu's polyomans, as he calls them, "conjugate" by joining to form a larger polyomino. As might be expected, only polyomans of the same size and shape are able to conjugate. (The mirror image of a polyomino is not considered different.) After the genetic information has been exchanged, the two replicas split apart. Each grows by adding new unit cells until it becomes twice as large, then it splits in half like an amoeba.

The figure below shows 13 different ways that bent trominoes (one of the two possible species of 3-cell animal) can conjugate in pairs to form 13 different hexominoes, or 6-cell forms. Actually, there is a 14th way, not shown, that a pair can conjugate. How quickly can you determine the missing shape? Put another way, draw a hexomino that is not a rotation or a mirror reflection of any of the 13 shown, and which can be divided into two bent trominoes. If you can't, look at the First Answers section.

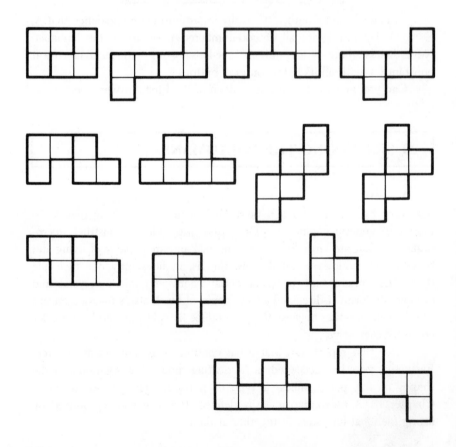

21 INNER PLANETS QUIZ

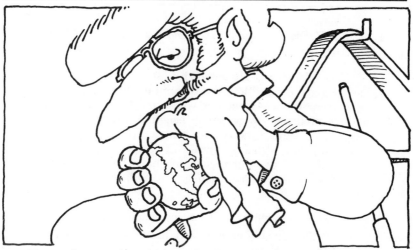

For a change of pace, try your brain on these puzzling questions about the four planets that are closest to the Sun.

1. Mercury. Many science fiction yarns have had as their setting the "twilight zone" of Mercury—a ring-like region of perpetual gloaming between the blazing hot side of Mercury and its freezing side of eternal night. Some notable examples: Larry Niven's "The Coldest Planet," Alan Nourse's "Brightside Crossing," Robert Silverberg's "Twilight Belt," and "The Twilight Planet" by Arthur J. Cox. Mercury's twilight zone has vanished totally from recent science fiction: Why?

2. Venus. You are on the surface of Venus. Thick clouds obscure the stars, but you know the Earth is directly overhead and the Sun is on the western horizon. Is the Sun rising or setting? As the planet rotates, will the Earth move east or west across the Venusian sky?

3. Earth. Imagine that the Earth is reduced to the size of a billiard ball, with all its mountains and valleys reduced proportionately. You wipe off the salty moisture with a towel, then run your fingers over the ball's surface. Would you be able to feel the mountains and ocean basins? If the Earth's orbit is drawn to scale on a sheet of paper the size of this page, would you be able to tell that the path was an ellipse?

4. Mars. I'll bet you didn't know that there are faces of two Martian monsters on a dollar bill. Of course no animal life now flourishes on Mars, so these must be creatures that inhabited that planet before it ran out of water. To find the monsters you have to pleat the bill a certain way.

These questions are answered and four more are raised in the First Answers section.

22

22 PUZZLES IN FLATLAND

In Arthur C. Clarke's *Childhood's End* (Chapter 18) we learn about Hexanerax 2:

> The planet was absolutely flat. Its enormous gravity had long ago crushed into one uniform level the mountains of its fiery youth—mountains whose mightiest peaks had never exceeded a few meters in height. Yet there was life here, for the surface was covered with a myriad geometrical patterns that crawled and moved and changed their color. It was a world of two dimensions, inhabited by beings who could be no more than a fraction of a centimeter in thickness.

Is it possible that intelligent life actually could evolve in a two-dimensional world? If the unreality of absolutely flat shapes troubles you, think of them (as in Clarke's description) as having an extremely small thickness, like cardboard shapes sliding about on a flat surface.

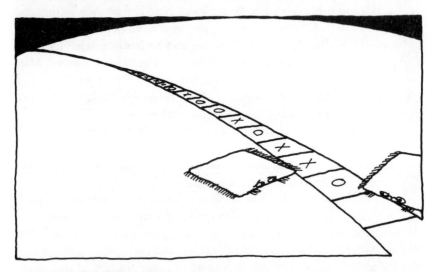

Until a few years ago it was assumed that no flat world could be physically real. Edwin Abbott had written his famous novel *Flatland* in 1884, and Charles Hinton in 1907 constructed a more plausible planar universe in *An Episode of Flatland*, subtitled "How a plane folk discovered the third dimension." Both novels were amusing fantasies. No one took seriously the notion that life in any form, let alone intelligent life, could possibly flourish in a two-dimensional universe.

22

The bombshell came in 1979 when Alexander Keewatin Dewdney, a computer scientist at the University of Western Ontario, published his surprising monograph on *Two-Dimensional Science and Technology*. In it he showed in astonishing detail how it was logically possible for a two-dimensional world to exist—a universe with a solar system, laws of physics, atomic matter, earthlike weather, intelligent life, and machines that could do almost anything our machines do. My column about this in *Scientific American* (July 1980) produced a flood of letters, many from top scientists, with hundreds of ingenious suggestions about flat technology.

Drawing on this material, and adding more ideas of his own, Dewdney wrote one of the most amazing tours de force in the history of science fiction: a novel called *The Planiverse* (Poseidon, 1984). This richly illustrated, funny book tells how the author and his students made computer contact with a two-dimensional being named Yendred. (Change the *r* to *w* and you get Dewdney backward.) Yendred eventually provided a detailed account of Arde, a circular planet on the rim of which he lives. (Dewdney, by the way, now writes the Computer Recreations department of *Scientific American*.)

We three-dimensional creatures find it convenient to play mathematical games on paper or two-dimensional boards. It's only natural to assume that flatlanders would find it convenient to play their games on "boards" of one dimension—that is, on lines. Surprisingly, many of our traditional games have nontrivial one-dimensional analogs. In his novel, Dewdney introduces one-dimensional go, and in my column on the planiverse I discussed linear forms of checkers and chess. Even linear ticktactoe (TTT) is not trivial. Flatlanders could distinguish the two marks by making one line segment long and the other short, or by using pencils of two colors or flat counters of different colors or shapes.

So far as I know, linear TTT has never been fully analyzed. It is played on a finite row of *n* cells, players alternating *X*s and *O*s, and the first to get three of his marks in a row is the winner. The second player cannot win if both sides play their best, but he can always force a draw. This is true also if the game is played in reverse—first to get three in a row loses.

If both players use the *same* mark, say *X*, it is called one-color TTT. Draws are obviously impossible. The first player can win on all boards with an odd number of cells by taking the middle cell and then playing symmetrically opposite each of his opponent's moves until he sees a chance to win. But if the board has *even* length the game is extremely difficult to analyze in normal form, and the reverse form on all boards (even or odd) is even worse. Winners have been determined by computer programs for boards of small length, but a general strategy (if there is one) remains undiscovered for the normal game on even boards and the reverse game on all boards. (See my discussion of the game in Chapter 12 of *Time Travel and Other Mathematical Bewilderments*.)

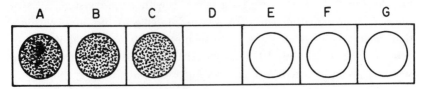

According to Yendred, flatlanders have hundreds of traditional counter-moving puzzles that use a linear "board." Consider, for example, the row of seven cells shown above. Put three pennies on cells *A*, *B*, *C* as shown, and three dimes on *E*, *F*, *G*. You are allowed to move in one of two ways: either *slide* to an adjacent empty cell in either direction, or *jump* (as in checkers) in either direction to an empty cell immediately beyond. Jumped pieces are not removed. The task is to make the dimes and pennies change places in the fewest number of moves.

The minimum possible is 15. See if you can make the exchange in 15 moves before looking at the solution in the First Answers section.

23 DIRAC'S SCISSORS

Paul Adrien Maurice Dirac was one of the great creative geniuses of modern quantum theory. In this chapter I wish to introduce a delightful topological puzzle involving a pair of scissors and some string. Dirac invented it when he was in his twenties to help explain one of the strangest of all the properties of the electron.

If you rotate a chair 360 degrees, it returns to its former state with respect to everything in the room. But if an electron is rotated 360 degrees, it does *not* return to the same state as before. It has to be given another full turn, 720 degrees in all, to bring it back to its former state with respect to its surroundings.

It is impossible to understand why this is so without getting into the advanced mathematics of quantum mechanics. Finding that his beginning students were made uncomfortable by such a weird property of certain particles, Dirac thought of a way to demonstrate something analogous. I first learned about Dirac's scissors, as his puzzle has been called, in 1959

23

when I was writing the Mathematical Games column in *Scientific American*. I wrote to Dirac about it, and one of my treasured possessions is his terse reply from Cambridge University:

Dear Mr. Gardner:

I am sorry I was too busy to answer your letter earlier. I first thought of the problem of the strings about 1929. I used it to illustrate a property of rotations, that two rotations of a body about an axis can be continuously deformed, through a set of motions which each end up with the original position, into no motion at all.

It is a consequence of this property of rotations that a spinning body can have half a quantum of angular momentum, but cannot have any other fraction of a quantum.

Yours sincerely
P.A.M. Dirac

Dirac's last sentence refers to the fact that the spin of all particles known as fermions is plus or minus 1/2 depending on the direction of spin. Regrettably, this is not the place to speak about the mystery of particle spin, or the way James Blish exploits it in his science-fiction novels in the working of his antigravity device, the "spindizzy." Spin is something vaguely like the spin of a top, but impossible to visualize or to explain in terms of classical physics.

At this point please stop reading and get a pair of scissors and a supply of string. You'll need two pieces of string, each about ten feet long. Pass each through a handle of the scissors, then tie the ends to make a loop. Stand on the loops as shown in the cartoon, so that when you raise the scissors to the level of your face the loops will produce four untwisted strands of cord running from scissors to floor.

Hold the scissors vertically, pointing toward the ceiling, then give the scissors a full turn of 360 degrees (in either direction) around a vertical axis. This will, of course, twist the cords.

Is it possible to untwist the cords without rotating the scissors in any way? You may translate the scissors about in space, and manipulate the strings as you please (without of course taking them from under your shoes), but the scissors must always keep the same orientation in space. The answer is that it is not possible to untangle the cords. You will be able to alter the way the string is tangled, but no amount of manipulation of the strings can bring the structure back to its original state.

After you have convinced yourself that the task is impossible, go back to the original untangled position. Now give the scissors *two* full turns (720 degrees) in either direction. Believe it or not, it is now possible to return the scissors and string to their original state without rotating the scissors in any way! To a topologist this means that after two full rotations of the scissors, the topological structure of scissors and string, relative to you and everything else in the room, has not been altered.

If you are unable to manipulate the string and scissors so as to remove the tangle—remember, the scissors must always point upward and not be turned in any way—you'll find the surprising solution in the First Answers section.

24 BULL'S-EYES AND PRATFALLS

Considering the fact that thousands of predictions are made every year in SF stories around the globe, it is not surprising that there are occasional hits of startling accuracy, like shooting a shotgun at a target. Of course there are even more whopping misses. Sometimes hits and misses accompany one another. Jules Verne scored a fantastic hit when he had the first spaceship shot around the moon from a spot in Florida, but his ship was blasted off by a gigantic underground cannon. Hundreds of SF tales anticipated moon walks. As far as I know, only one guessed that the first walk would be watched on Earth's television screens: *Prelude to Space*, a novel by Arthur C. Clarke. It was first published in *Galaxy* (February 1951), and later reprinted under other titles.

It would be no small task to draw up a complete list of H.G. Wells's hits and misses. His most spectacular success was in the chapter that opens

The World Set Free (1914)—reprinted in my anthology *The Sacred Beetle and Other Great Essays in Science*—in which Wells tells how the atom was first split. The novel has the second world war starting in the forties, and there is a graphic description of an "atomic bomb" (yes, Wells used the term!) dropped on the enemy. But the bomb is held by a person who drops it through an opening in the bottom of a plane.

In his 1902 collection of prophetic essays, *Anticipations*, Wells correctly foresaw wide asphalt thruways, looping over and under at intersections, and with a dividing barrier between opposite directions of traffic. A chapter on twentieth-century warfare is amazingly accurate in many ways, but the air battles are fought by men in balloons, and Wells had this to say about submarines: "I must confess that my imagination, in spite even of spurring, refuses to see any sort of submarine doing anything but suffocate its crew and founder at sea." It has been justly said that Wells hit the mark more often in his SF than in his nonfiction. In *Social Forces in England and America*, published the same year as *The World Set Free*, he speaks of "the tapping of atomic energy, but I give two hundred years before that."

For decades I have been trying to gather a complete run of Hugo Gernsback's marvelous *Science and Invention*, especially during its golden age of the twenties. The magazine's lurid covers are an amusing mix of hits and misses. Among the hits: helicopters carrying girders for skyscraper construction, the use of flame throwers in warfare, and (my favorite) a man and woman embracing, with wires attached to various parts of their bodies to measure heart beat, respiration, perspiration, and so on. It illustrated Gernsback's article on the scientific study of sex. Among the

24

misses: a giant robot policeman, and a picture of what a Martian would look like. Gernsback's *Ralph 124C41 +* is probably the worst SF novel ever published (it ends with the awful pun "one to foresee for one"), yet it also contains some of the most accurate predictions ever made in such a novel.

If you're interested in outlandish misses about the future, I recommend *The Experts Speak: The Definitive Compendium of Authoritative Misinformation*, by Christopher Cerf and Victor Navasky. On hits by SF writers, see the article "Prediction" in *The Science Fiction Encyclopedia*, edited by Peter Nicholls. Listed below, from my collection, are some outstanding instances of astonishing anticipations by writers outside the SF field. See if you can guess some of the authors and the centuries in which they wrote.

1. "Clothes hung up on a shore which waves break upon become moist, and then get dry if spread out in the sun. Yet it has not been seen in what way the moisture of water has sunk into them nor again in what way this has been dispelled by heat. The moisture therefore is dispersed into small particles which the eyes are quite unable to see."

2. "The primary elements of matter are, in my opinion, perfectly indivisible and nonextended points; they are so scattered in an immense vacuum that every two of them are separated from one another by a definite interval."

3. "... two lesser stars, or satellites, which revolved about Mars, whereof the innermost is distant from the centre of the primary planet exactly three of the diameters, and the outermost five; the former revolves in the space of ten hours, and the latter in twenty-one and an half."

4. "If Mr. B will drink a great deal of water, the acrimony that corrodes his bowels will be diluted, if the cause be only acrimony; but I suspect dysenteries to be produced by animalculae which I know not how to kill."

5. "I know a way by which 'tis easy enough to hear one speak through a wall a yard thick ... I can assure the reader that I have by the help of distended wire propagated the sound to a very considerable distance in an instant, or with as seemingly quick a motion as that of light ... and this not only in a straight line, or direct, but in one bended in many angles."

6. "Such changes in the superficial parts of the globe seemed to me unlikely to happen if the Earth were solid to the centre. I therefore imagined that the internal parts might be a fluid more dense, and of greater specific gravity than any of the solids we are acquainted with; which therefore might swim in or upon that fluid. Thus the surface of the

globe would be a shell, capable of being broken and disordered by the violent movements of the fluid on which it rested."

7. "Would it be too bold to imagine that, in the great length of time since the world began to exist, perhaps millions of ages before the commencement of the history of mankind—would it be too bold to imagine that all warm-blooded animals have arisen from one *living filament*, which the great First Cause emdued with animality, with the power of acquiring new parts, attended with new propensities, directed by irritations, sensations, volitions, and associations, and thus possessing the faculty of continuing to improve by its own inherent activity and of delivering down these improvements by generation to its posterity, world without end?"

8.   For I dipt into the future, far as human eye could see,
      Saw the Vision of the world, and all the wonders that would be;

      Saw the heavens fill with commerce, argosies of magic sails,
      Pilots of the purple twilight, dropping down with costly bales;

      Heard the heavens fill with shouting, and there rain'd a ghastly dew
      From the nation's airy navies grappling in the central blue;

      Far along the world-wide whisper of the south-wind rushing warm,
      With the standards of the peoples plunging thro' the thunder-storm;

      Till the war-drum throbb'd no longer, and the battle-flags were furl'd
      In the Parliament of man, the Federation of the world.

25 FLARP FLIPS ANOTHER FIVER

Lieutenant Flarp, navigation officer on the *USS Bagel*, Ensign Pulver, and Tanya had just finished their first drinks in the spacious lounge of the *Bagel*, earth's largest spaceship. Tanya had recently turned twenty—a flaxen haired young lady who was as pretty as she was bright. Her father, Colonel Couth, headed the spaceship's computer division.

Flarp took a fiver from his pocket. It was a large coin, worth five dollars, made of a light-weight metallic alloy.

"Let's flip to see whether you or I buy the round," said Flarp to Pulver. "But instead of flipping once, I'll toss the coin five times. If the number of heads is even, I'll pay. If the number is odd, you pay."

"Hold on!" exclaimed Pulver. "You must think I'm a dummy. There are three ways to get an odd number of heads—one head, three heads, or five. But there are only *two* ways to get an even number—two heads or four. The odds are three to two in your favor."

"I don't think you're a dummy," said Flarp, smiling. "But I do think you don't know much about probability theory."

Flarp turned over the paper mat under his drink. "The number of equally possible outcomes of five tosses is two to the fifth power, or thirty-two. I'll list all of them."

Flarp's Chart

	No.					
	1.	H	H	H	H	H
✓	2.	H	H	H	H	T
✓	3.	H	H	H	T	H
	4.	H	H	H	T	T
✓	5.	H	H	T	H	H
	6.	H	H	T	H	T
	7.	H	H	T	T	H
✓	8.	H	H	T	T	T
✓	9.	H	T	H	H	H
	10.	H	T	H	H	T
	11.	H	T	H	T	H
✓	12.	H	T	H	T	T
	13.	H	T	T	H	H
✓	14.	H	T	T	H	T

✔15.	H	T	T	T	H
16.	H	T	T	T	T
✔17.	T	H	H	H	H
18.	T	H	H	H	T
19.	T	H	H	T	H
✔20.	T	H	H	T	T
21.	T	H	T	H	H
✔22.	T	H	T	H	T
✔23.	T	H	T	T	H
24.	T	H	T	T	T
25.	T	T	H	H	H
✔26.	T	T	H	H	T
✔27.	T	T	H	T	H
28.	T	T	H	T	T
✔29.	T	T	T	H	H
30.	T	T	T	H	T
31.	T	T	T	T	H
✔32.	T	T	T	T	T

Flarp quickly wrote down the 32 combinations. He was able to do this rapidly by adopting a simple procedure. He alternated *H*s and *T*s (for heads and tails) in the fifth column, alternated pairs of *H*s and *T*s in the fourth column, quadruplets in the third column, sets of eight in the second column, and two sets of 16 in the first column. Then he checked off all the combinations with an even number of heads, as shown in Flarp's Chart, including of course the *TTTTT* case with the even number 0.

Pulver counted the checks. There were 16, exactly half of 32. While Pulver was studying the chart with a mystified look on his face, Tanya burst out laughing.

"You didn't have to go to all that trouble," she said to Flarp. "There's a ridiculously easy way to prove that the bet's fair without writing down a single combination."

Can you guess what Tanya has in mind? If not, turn to the First Answers section.

---

26 BLUES IN THE NIGHT

Chromo is a small planet inhabited by three races of humanoids. Each has a distinctive skin color: pink, blue, or green.

A murder trial is in progress on Chromo, and a police officer is testifying. All policemen on Chromo are, of course, blue.

"We got this message at headquarters," said the cop, "that a woman in the pink section of the city was screaming like she was being attacked. I arrived at the apartment building just in time to see a green man run out the front door. I gave chase, but the man got away."

"Are you positive he was green?" asked the attorney for the defense. The suspect on trial for the woman's murder was a green.

"Well," said the cop, massaging the side of his blue face, "I can't say I'm absolutely sure. It was in the middle of the night and the lights on that street are not so good. He could have been blue."

The defense lawyer then introduced to the court the results of a test that had been made of the officer's ability to distinguish a blue from a green (he never confused a green or a blue with a pink) under the lighting conditions that had prevailed in the street during the night of the murder. The policeman had accurately recognized a man's color 80 percent of the time. In other words, he was mistaken one time out of five.

A few days later the jurors found themselves debating the following question: How probable is it that the man seen fleeing the scene of the crime was actually blue?

"I can't see any difficulty here," said one of the pink women on the jury. "The policeman is right 4/5 of the time and mistaken 1/5 of the time. He said he thought the man was green. So the probability he really was a green is 4/5, and the probability he was a blue is 1/5."

"You couldn't be more wrong," said a green juror. "You forget that in this city blues outnumber greens by a ratio of 85 to 15."

"I know that," said a pink juror. "So what? How can if affect the way we estimate the probability that the policeman made a mistake when he said the man was green?"

Which juror is right? It's a very tricky question, and likely to give you a headache when you think about it. The fact that in the city there are 85 blues for every 15 greens is background information that in Bayesian probability theory is called the "base rate." Is it relevant to the question? Or should one reason, as the pink juror did, that the probability of the fleeing man being blue is 1/5? For an analysis, see First Answers section.

27 AGAIN, HOW'S THAT AGAIN?

It had been almost a year since I last visited my friend Fred ("How's that again?") Flanagan, the well known science-fiction author who lives at the edge of Paradox Lake in Essex County, New York. Fred is always a good source of amusing material. Not only does he own a vast collection of mind-bending paradoxes, but he speaks in a constant stream of paradoxical remarks.

When I last saw Fred (see Chapter 14) he had shaved his head and was sporting a bleached-white beard, but when I called on him in November he had reversed the two growths. His face was clean-shaven, but thick black hair hung below his shoulders. A large button pinned to his dirty sweater said:

BUT = TRUTH.

"I don't get it," I said.

"Bee—you—tee, beauty," Fred replied. "It's that marvelous line from Keats."

"I never really understood what Keats meant," I said, smiling.

"I used to be uncertain about it too," said Fred. "Now I'm not so sure."

I pointed to a large square board on the wall. Painted on it in heavy black lines was the picture shown below. "What's *that* all about?"

"The pie has a missing slice," said Fred as he walked over to the picture, "but where is it?"

He rotated the board 180 degrees (it had been mounted on the wall by a central peg). There was the slice!

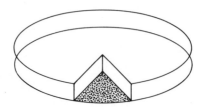

"What an amazing illusion!" I exclaimed.

"Not really," said Fred. "It just looks like one."

How's that again?"

"I mean that our brain is so used to seeing pies from above—never upside-down from below—that it makes the best inductive bet it can in the light of experience. That's why craters on the moon look like mountains if you hold a moon photograph so the sunlight hits the craters from below."

Of all the strange paradoxes Fred told me about on that cold November afternoon, the strangest involved the movement of a chess king on a 3 × 3 chessboard. You'll have to follow the description carefully because it's not an easy argument.

Take a look at the board shown on the facing page. The king is not allowed to move diagonally—only up, down, left, and right, and just one cell per move. We symbolize its moves by U, D, L, R.

The king may make a move that bumps into the border of the board. When this happens the king stays on the same cell and we put a line over the letter to represent the bump. For example, if the king starts on 4 and moves $\overline{D}\overline{D}$ this means that it first moves to 7, then tries to go down again but bumps. If the king starts on 4 and moves $\overline{L}\,\overline{L}$ it bumps twice in the same direction, remaining on 4. If it starts at 3 and moves $\overline{U}\,\overline{R}$ it bumps twice in two different directions, remaining on 3.

1	2	3
4	5	6
7	8	9

Assume that someone in another room has put the king on any square and made two moves at random. You are told only the notation. Can you always deduce the number of the cell on which the king is now standing? Sometimes you can. For example, if given the moves $\overline{U}\,\overline{L}$ you know the king must be on 1 because this sequence of moves cannot put the king on any other cell.

Now for two crucial definitions. We call a cell *undecidable* if there is *no* two-move sequence from which we can deduce that the king ends on that cell. If there *is* such a sequence, the cell is called *decidable*.

Suppose the person in the other room tells you he has moved the king twice, and it now rests on an undecidable cell. Is it possible for him to speak the truth when he makes such a statement? Here is Flanagan's proof that it is not possible, because there are *no* undecidable cells.

No corner cell can be undecidable. $\overline{U}\,\overline{L}$ renders 1 decidable because that sequence of moves cannot put the king on any other cell. $\overline{U}\,\overline{R}$ makes 3 decidable. $\overline{D}\,\overline{L}$ makes 7 decidable, and $\overline{D}\,\overline{R}$ makes 9 decidable. The king cannot be on a corner cell.

No side cell $(2, 4, 6, 8)$ can be undecidable. Consider $U\overline{U}$. It cannot mean a move from 4 to 1, or from 6 to 3, because in each case it would put the king on a corner cell, and we have ruled out the possibility of the king being on a corner. $U\overline{U}$ can only mean that the king goes from 5 to 2, which makes 2 decidable. Similar reasoning makes 4 decidable (by $L\overline{L}$), 6 decidable by ($R\overline{R}$), and 8 decidable (by $D\overline{D}$). The king cannot be on a side cell.

Only cell 5 remains. Since we have deduced that the king must be on 5, it too has become decidable. *All* cells are decidable. The person who said he had moved the king to an undecidable cell spoke falsely because we have found a contradiction in what he said.

Now for the crunch. After proving that no cell is undecidable, Flanagan proceeded to show, by equally iron logic, that all cells except the corners are undecidable! To see how, look at the First Answers section.

28 ALICE IN BEELAND

There are no bees in Lewis Carroll's *Alice* books unless you include the elephants in the first paragraph of the insect chapter of *Through the Looking-Glass*. At first Alice thought they were bees because she saw them in the distance using their trunks to extract honey from giant flowers. Nevertheless, there is a thriving colony of highly intelligent bees in Wonderland.

"How curious," said Alice as she watched two worker bees playing chess on a triangular board tesselated like a honeycomb. "On the other side of the mirror we play chess on squares."

"I'm aware of that, honey," said the bee playing the black pieces. "But we find that square cells make a very dull game. Your rooks move only in four directions. Our rooks move in six."

"Mr. Dodgson showed me a marvelous puzzle on our chessboard," said Alice. "The problem is to put eight queens on the board so no queen attacks another."

"I know the puzzle well," said the bee playing white. "On our chessboard we have a similar problem of nonattacking rooks."

After the game ended, Herbert—the bee who played white—used the honeycomb board to show Alice what the mathematicians of Beeland have discovered about the combinatorial problem of nonattacking bee-rooks. The figure on the facing page shows how a maximum number of bee-rooks can be placed on triangular boards with sides of 1 through 7 so that no rook attacks another. The largest number that can be put on the order-8 board, shown blank, is five. Can you find a way to do it before looking at the First Answers section?

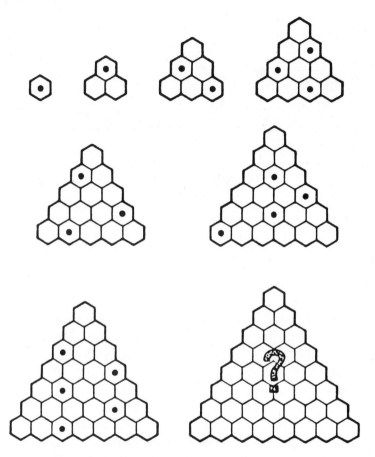

29 HUSTLE OFF TO BUFFALO

The time: mid-twenty-first century. Place: a stretch of gleaming highway between New York City and Buffalo. I was on another out-of-body trip to the future in my car, the Hustle, in the sixth lane of a standard twenty-lane thruway. As readers may recall from Chapter 8, my Chinese-built car contained the latest protein-based supercomputer. It was connected to sensory devices that enabled it to see, hear, and even smell. It could engage in intelligent conversation.

29

As usual, when on long boring trips, I liked to let the Hustle take over the controls. We would then while away the hours by asking each other interesting questions in the areas of mathematics and word play. The car is particularly fond of puzzles that relate to its experiences on thruways.

"I've just determined," said the Hustle, "that we have passed the halfway point on our trip to Buffalo. To be precise, the difference between the distance we've gone and the distance we have yet to go is precisely 70 km. Can you tell me how many more kilometers we have to travel to raise that difference to 100 km?"

"That's easy," I said. "We have to go thirty more kilometers."

"Wrong again!" shouted the Hustle, following the shout with its infuriating metallic chuckle. "The answer is 15 km."

Of course Hus was right. I had answered too hastily. "Okay, pal. You caught me on that one. Now here's one for you. A car passed us about thirty minutes ago with a bumper sticker that said 'I love New York'—except *love* was replaced by the playing-card symbol of a heart."

"I'm familiar with the sticker," the car said, "I see lots of them around the New York City area."

"The other day," I went on, "I saw a bumper sticker that started with the word *I*, followed by the card symbol for a spade. Can you guess what followed?"

The Hustle searched its memory banks for several minutes before it gave up.

"The answer," I said, "is 'I ♠ my cats.'"

"I spade my cats?" said the Hustle. "It doesn't make sense."

I was surprised that Hus failed to get the pun. It listened silently while I explained.

"How about some tough geographical teasers?" I suggested. Hus knew everything in the latest world atlas, and geographical riddles were one of its specialities.

"Very well," said the car after a few seconds. "You used the adjective *tough*. It ends in *G* and *H*. How quickly can you name a state ending in *G*, and another state ending in *H*?"

I got the first one, but not the second. Both are given in the First Answers section.

30 RAY PALMER'S ARCADE

Raymond Dero Palmer, as some readers may recall, is a gnomelike little man about four feet tall, with a cherub's face and watery blue eyes. He has a habit of moving from city to city, running shops that carry curious merchandise. I once bought a Klein bottle from him that contained a genie. It had been several years since I purchased some old SF magazines from one of his shops in Chicago (see Chapter 15 of my *Puzzles from Others Worlds*).

I recently had occasion to walk through the German district on Manhattan's upper east side when I passed an arcade of computer games. The sign above the door said "Ray Palmer's Fantasy and Science Fiction Galaxy."

The large room was almost totally dark, illuminated only by the fluorescent screens of the games. It was jammed with teenagers, mostly boys, and noisy with all the buzzes, whistles, and other weird sounds that came from the machines. All the games had SF or fantasy themes. Most were of the Star Wars type, but some involved capturing bug-eyed monsters, outwitting evil sorcerers, exploring strange planets, and so on.

Ray was there, wearing an apron, its large pockets filled with coins for making change. He had grown a long gray beard since I last saw him, making him look even more gnomelike.

I wandered around the room, watching games over the shoulders of players. In back of the arcade was an elevator. A sign on front said: KEEP OUT! PRIVATE USE ONLY. On the street I had noticed that the arcade was in a low flat building that had only one floor. Where could this elevator possibly go?

Always eager for adventure, I pulled open the door and stepped inside. There were just two large buttons, low on the front wall. One had *dn* printed on it. The other had exactly the same two letters inverted: *up*. I pressed the *dn* button. Through a small glass window I saw an angry Palmer rushing toward the elevator, but he was too late.

Watching through the window I could see that the elevator was rapidly gaining speed, and I could feel the acceleration by a lessening of my weight. The elevator soon settled down to a uniform rate. I couldn't believe it! For a full five minutes it sped downward.

My knees buckled as the elevator slowed to a stop, then something even more fantastic happened. The elevator began to move sideways! This continued for a full ten minutes before it resumed its vertical descent. My watch indicated a passage of almost 20 minutes before the elevator stopped and the door opened.

I stepped out into an enormous cavern. It was laced with gigantic stalagmites and stalactites, and lit by a strange purple glow that seemed part of the atmosphere. A midget humanoid, even smaller than Palmer, approached. He (I assumed it was male) was nude but totally covered with black hair. He had a nose something like an elephant's, and two elephant-like ears.

"Welcome," he said, making an uncouth hand gesture, "to the land of the deros."

Of course I knew about the deros. They were supposed to be wicked creatures who lived underground, as described in Richard Shaver's notorious SF tales of the late forties. I had always assumed that Shaver's stories were pure fiction, yet here I was, talking to a dero!

"You are Martin Gardner," said the dero, "and you contribute puzzles to a shabby little pulp magazine that bears the name of that arch-skeptic Isaac Asimov."

30

"How in hades did you know that?"

The dero smiled with his mouth, though not with his evil eyes. "We have extraordinary psi powers. My remote vision saw you enter Palmer's elevator. I checked the IDs in your wallet."

"My knees," I said, "are still wobbly from that wild elevator ride."

"Ah yes," said the dero, "Inertia. It's the same as gravity, you know. Einstein thought he discovered that equivalence, but we have known about it for fifty thousand years."

"I'm familiar with the principle of equivalence. After all, I wrote a popular book about relativity. Newton would have assumed that inertial forces inside an accelerating elevator proved that motion is absolute. You can't assume the elevator is fixed, and the universe moving, because then what would cause the inertial forces?"

"Right," said the dero, "As you know, Einstein used the elevator thought-experiment to explain why that isn't so. Assume your elevator is at rest, and the universe accelerating up or down. The accelerating universe generates gravity fields that produce the inertial effects."

"You do indeed know your relativity theory," I responded. "As I said in my book, it's not a question of which is *really* moving, the elevator or the universe. It's like asking whether ice-cream is on top of the pie, or the pie under the ice-cream. Only the relative motion is significant. If you take the universe as a fixed frame of reference—by far the simplest thing to do —the effects in the elevator are called inertial. If you take the elevator as fixed (which of course is much less convenient), the forces in the elevator are called gravitational. The tensor equations describing the field are identical in both cases. There is only *one* field, but you can talk about it in two different ways."

The dero smiled his mirthless smile again. "Before you go—and we can't let you stay any longer—here's a question for your moronic readers. Imagine yourself in an elevator with opaque walls. The gravity field is the same as on Earth. The question arises: Are you at rest on a planet with a g field, or are you in an elevator accelerating upward at a rate that simulates the g field? Remember, the elevator is opaque. You can't observe anything outside. Assume the elevator is large enough to hold whatever sophisticated measuring devices you need. Is there an experiment you can perform that will distinguish between the two possibilities—an upward accelerating elevator, and one at rest on a planet?"

I knew the answer, but before I could reply, six other deros appeared on the scene. They forced me into the elevator, pushed the *up* button, and closed the door. The elevator suddenly filled with a purplish vapor. Two whiffs, and I passed out.

When I came to, the elevator was at rest and the door was slowly opening. On the wall I saw a conventional column of buttons for many floors. When I stepped out, I found myself on the top floor of Macy's department store.

What's the answer to the dero's question? As Einstein explained, you can't use light rays to detect the difference, because light, like material objects, is affected by gravity and inertia in identical ways. Nevertheless, there is a simple test you can make. Assume that the gravitational field of the planet is as if all its mass were concentrated at one point at its center, and that the attraction due to the elevator and to any masses moving along with it is zero. For a description of the test, see the First Answers section.

31 PUZZLE FLAGS ON MARS

Before the middle of the 21st century, hundreds of colonies were flourishing on the red planet, each under an enormous transparent dome that permitted sunlight to pass through, held the artificial atmosphere, and allowed for farming. Each colony had its own flag on top of its dome.

Recreational mathematicians can find puzzles in almost anything with a mathematical structure, and flag patterns are no exceptions. I've made here a selection of four Martian flags that present simple but fascinating puzzles. Moreover, they are puzzles not yet well known.

Consider first the flag of a colony called Bowleria, founded by a group of Americans who had a passion for bowling. As you see, the design

31

consists of ten circles arranged like a set of bowling pins viewed from above (top left). Your task is to shade four of the circles so that no three of the unshaded circles mark the corners of an equilateral triangle. There is essentially only one way to do it.

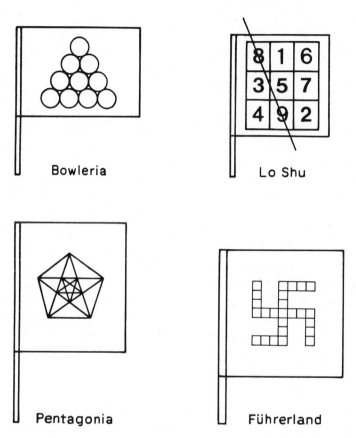

Bowleria

Lo Shu

Pentagonia

Führerland

Incidentally, it is *not* possible to color the circles with two colors so that no three circles of the same color are at the corners of an equilateral triangle. Proving this is harder than the problem given. If you're interested, you'll find a proof in Chapter 7 of my *Unexpected Hanging*.

Consider next the flag of a Chinese colony on Mars called Lo Shu. *Lo shu* is the ancient Chinese name for the classic 3 × 3 magic square shown in the picture (top right). Aside from rotations and reflections, it is the only way the first nine consecutive counting numbers can be arranged so each row, each column, and each of the two main diagonals, adds to 15. Your task is to draw a single straight line across the *lo shu* in such a way that it passes through the interiors of a group of cells with the largest possible sum. In the picture you see a line crossing four cells. Their sum is 25, but you can do better.

Here are two more questions about 3×3 magic squares, both easily answered if you have the right *aha!* insight. Can you make a 3×3 magic square with the consecutive *even* numbers: 2, 4, 6, 8, 10, 12, 14, 16, 18? Can such a square be made with the consecutive *odd* numbers: 1, 3, 5, 7, 9, 11, 13, 15, 17?

Our third puzzle is based on the flag of Pentagonia, colonized in the 2030s by a band of Spanish explorers. The flag is shown at the lower left of the illustration. Its five-sided diagram is closely related to the pentagram of the ancient Greek Pythagorean brotherhood. It has many curious geometrical properties, but your task is merely to count the number of different capital A letters—the initial of Asimov—that are in the diagram.

We must carefully define what is meant by an A. The two line segments that meet at the top must be equal in length, and the cross bar must cut off from them an isosceles triangle. The A may be as wide or narrow as you please. Its legs below the cross bar may be short or long. All five nodes on the A must be nodes on the diagram, and of course the letter may be turned in any orientation.

When this problem first appeared in an Argentine game and puzzle magazine called *Cacumen* (December 1984), the editors gave an answer of 25. Readers were quick to point out that this was wrong. There are more than 25 A's in the pattern.

Our final puzzle, the hardest of the four, is based on the swastika shown on the flag at lower right. This is the flag of Führerland, a colony founded on Mars by German neo-Nazis. Your task is to cut the swastika along the interior lines into the fewest number of pieces that can be rearranged to make a 5×5 square.

When this tricky dissection problem first appeared in the *Pi Mu Epsilon Journal* (Fall 1983), the proposer thought it could not be solved in fewer than five pieces. (One particularly pleasing solution is to cut a 5-cell Greek cross from the swastika's center, then fit the four truncated arms symmetrically around it.) To the proposer's great surprise, one reader, Emil Slowinski, came up with a four-piece dissection.

Speaking of swastikas, do you know how to make a Nazi cross with five matches? You stick four of them in his ear, then light them with the fifth! For answers to the other flag puzzles posed here, see the First Answers section.

32 THE VANISHING PLANK

The Black Tube, known to physicists as a John Wheeler "worm hole," has its entrance inside the black hole that spins at the center of the Milky Way Galaxy. The Tube extends along a fourth spatial coordinate through an infinity of parallel universes that are adjacent to one another like the leaves of a monstrous four-dimensional book. At the Tube's entrance is Aleph-Null Inn, named for the smallest of Georg Cantor's infinite hierarchy of transfinite numbers. (Aleph-null counts the set of integers: $1, 2, 3, 4, \ldots$.)

The Inn has an aleph-null infinity of rooms. This leads to many curious paradoxes, some of which have been discussed in the two previous book collections of my science-fiction puzzle tales. As you might expect, the Inn offers entertainment of a sort never seen in this world. There are, for example, skilled dancers, some with 20 legs, capable of executing an infinity of steps which get faster and faster, allowing the dance routine to be completed in a finite time. And there are marvelous singers, some with two mouths which allow them to sing duets with themselves. They enthrall audiences with "fractal" songs. These are melodies in which an infinity of notes are, like the dance steps, concluded in finite periods of time.

Aleph the Great, a magician who appears regularly at the Inn's cabaret, specializes in illusions based on infinite sets. We will consider one of his favorites—the incredible vanishing plank.

The plank is one meter long, six centimeters wide, and half a centimeter thick. It is not made of wood, but of a substance utterly unlike any in our galaxy. Here all matter is composed of discrete particles. But the Great Aleph's plank, made in another universe, is a dense continuum of infinitely divisible matter, more like the matter in Aristotle's physics than in the physics of the Greek atomists.

The Great Aleph begins his illusion by first causing the plank to float in midair above the stage. Then, using a cutting device that operates with ever-accelerating speed, the Great Aleph removes 1/4 of the plank from its center. The removed piece is discarded. He next removes a section of length 1/16 from the middle of each of the two remaining pieces. There are now four disconnected pieces. From the middle of each, a section of length 1/64 is taken. Thus at each step a section one-fourth of the previously removed length is taken from the center of all remaining sections, and this procedure is continued to infinity. The figure below shows the plank in cross section. The black portions are those sections removed during the first three steps.

1/64	1/16	1/64	1/4	1/64	1/16	1/64

The Mutilated Plank

The first step takes away 1/4 of the plank. The second step removes 1/16 + 1/16 or 1/8 of the original plank. The third step removes 1/64 + 1/64 + 1/64 + 1/64 or 1/16 of the original plank. The total amounts removed at each step form the infinite series $1/4 + 1/8 + 1/16 + 1/32 + \cdots$, which has a sum of 1/2. Each step is completed in a time interval that is the same as the amount of plank removed at that step. The first step takes 1/4 minute, the second step takes 1/8 minute, the third 1/16, and so on. Therefore the cutting task is completed in exactly half a minute. At the end of that time exactly half of the original plank has been removed.

Has the plank vanished or is some of it still there? For a "proof" it has vanished, see the First Answers section.

---

33   987654321

Each of the following nine questions can be answered quickly if you know some elementary theorems about the integers and have the right insights. Each concerns the same sequence of digits: 987654321. Try to answer the questions without the aid of a calculator.

9. A prime is a number divisible only by itself and 1. Prove that 987654321 is not a prime.

8. A factorial is the product of $1 \times 2 \times 3 \times \cdots \times n$, and is written $n!$ Prove that 987654321 is not a factorial.

7. Imagine that superbeings in some higher dimension play card games with a deck that consists of n cards, where n is our sequence 987654321 repeated one million times. We know from the answer to question 9 that the cards can be evenly divided among 9 or 3 players. Can they be evenly divided among 8, 7, 6, 5, 4, or 2 players?

6. Can they be evenly divided among 11 players?

5. Can they be evenly divided among 1000000001 players?

4. A perfect number is the sum of all its divisors, including 1 but not itself. Six is perfect because $6 = 1 + 2 + 3$, and 28 is perfect because $28 = 1 + 2 + 4 + 7 + 14$. It is not known if there is an infinity of perfect numbers or if an odd perfect number exists. By the end of 1986, only 30 perfect numbers had been identified.

Prove that 987654321 is not perfect.

3. An old number recreation has to do with adding plus or minus signs within the sequence 123456789, or within its reversal 987654321, to make the total a specified number. For instance, the only way to make the rising sequence total 100 with as few as three signs is $123 + 45 - 67 + 89 = 100$. You'll find all the solutions for 100, for both sequences, using any number of signs (including a minus sign in front of the first digit) in Chapter 6 of my *Magic Numbers of Dr. Matrix*. All solutions for 666, the Bible's number of the Beast, are given in Chapter 31 of my *Puzzles from Other Worlds*.

Your task is to insert seven signs within 987654321 to make the total zero.

2. Let's go back to question 7 where we considered the number produced by repeating the sequence 987654321 a million times. Do the first n digits of this sequence, where n is any integer less than or equal to nine million, ever form a prime?

1. Remove nine spades from a deck of cards, with values of ace through nine. You want to arrange them in an order that will permit the following spelling trick.

Hold the packet of nine cards, all face down, in your left hand. Transfer one card at a time from top to bottom, and with each transfer spell a letter of NINE. After the four cards have been moved to the bottom, turn over the top card. It is the nine of spades. Discard it. Spell EIGHT, transferring five cards to the bottom. The top card is now the eight of spades. Discard it and continue in this manner, spelling and discarding the 7, 6, 5, 4, 3, and 2 of spades. The ace is left in your hand.

You might suppose it unlikely that the nine cards can be arranged to permit such a curious spelling procedure, one that seems so unrelated to the numbers that are spelled. Actually, it is easy to find the correct arrangement in just a few minutes. How is it done? For answers and comments to items $9, 8, \ldots, 2, 1$, see the First Answers section.

34 TIME-REVERSED WORLDS

One of the monumental astronomical discoveries of the twenty-first century was made by Professor Alexander Graham Cracker, the noted British astrophysicist. Using advanced instrumentation attached to a radio telescope on a space station, he was the first to establish that half the galaxies in the universe are made of antimatter. Moreover, he found that in all those galaxies the direction of time is opposite to that of our Milky Way galaxy.

If there are sentient beings in these time-reversed galaxies, of course time for them seems to go the usual way. To them, it is *our* arrow of time that is reversed. The situation is analogous to the two worlds on opposite sides of the mirror in *Alice Through the Looking Glass*.

It was generally agreed among physicists that communication between the inhabitants of two worlds, each with a different time direction, would be impossible. Professor Cracker thought otherwise.

"What are you typing, Alex?" asked Ada Loveface, the professor's attractive research assistant.

"It's a treatise on communication between time-reversed worlds," Cracker replied. "My computer search at the library of the British Museum turned up a fascinating paper by a Scottish philosopher named Murray MacBeath. It appeared in a philosophical journal called *Synthese* more than fifty years ago. [Volume 56, 1983, pages 27–46.] In this paper MacBeath outlined a simple way that such communication could take place."

"That's ridiculous," said Ada. "How does MacBeath's scheme work?"

Cracker lifted his hands from the keyboard of his laser word processor and swiveled his chair around. "To simplify our thought experiment, let's assume the two worlds are alike in all respects except their time direction. Inhabitants speak the same language. Their days are the same time intervals. Imagine also that there is an enormous screen at the interface between the two worlds on which messages can instantaneously be placed and read by either side."

Ada reflected for a minute. "Fair enough. I know you have to make wild counterfactual assumptions in most thought experiments, but I can't see anything conceptually impossible in what you propose."

Cracker nodded. "I now program my computer on Day 1 to flash this message on the big screen." He pressed a button to call up the text on the monitor. The message began:

PLEASE ANSWER THE FOLLOWING QUESTIONS. BUT DON'T PUT YOUR REPLY ON THE SCREEN UNTIL 99 DAYS FROM NOW, YOUR TIME. WHEN YOU REPLY, ASK QUESTIONS OF YOUR OWN.

Ada looked puzzled.

"Here's the clever idea behind the plan," Cracker went on. "I set my computer to send the message on my Day 100."

Ada had a mind as quick as she was pretty. "I can see what's coming. Your correspondent, going the other way in time, sees your message 100 days *before* your Day 1. He delays his reply until *his* Day 99, which is *your* Day 2. So on your Day 2 you get a reply to the message your computer will send on your Day 100."

"Precisely," said Cracker, rubbing his hands and smiling. "And we can keep sending messages back and forth in see-saw fashion. I program my reply to go on the screen 98 days in *my* future. He programs his next reply to go on the screen 97 days in *his* future. I see it on my Day 3. We can keep sending questions and answers back and forth until the middle of the time period, after which an exchange becomes impossible. Of course there's no need to limit the conversation to 100 days. It can be 100 years, or as long as we want."

A slow grin spread over Ada's face. "Unfortunately, Alex, MacBeath's scheme has a whopping logical flaw. It can't possibly work."

After Ada explained the flaw, Professor Cracker sighed, slapped his forehead, and erased from the computer everything he had written.

What flaw did Ada have in mind? [Section Answers First the in explained is flaw the.]

35 THE WISDOM OF SOLOMON

According to the Old Testament (I Kings 4:31) Solomon "was wiser than all men." We all know the story (I Kings 3) about how he settled a bitter dispute between two harlots, each claiming to be the mother of a newborn baby. Solomon solemnly proposed slicing the child in half with a sword and giving a half to each claimant. One harlot agreed. Solomon awarded the child to the other woman when she offered to give up the baby if Solomon would only spare its life.

Both I Kings 10 and II Chronicles 9 tell how the fire-worshiping Queen of Sheba (or "Queen of the South" as Jesus called her in Matthew 12:42) made a pilgrimage to Jerusalem to test Solomon's wisdom with "hard questions." The Old Testament records no details concerning the questions, but there are many colorful legends about them in the Talmud, in other ancient Hebrew documents, in the Koran and its early commentaries, and in Islamic folklore.

One legend says that Balkis (as she is called in the Koran) introduced a group of boys and girls, all dressed alike. Solomon was asked to separate the sexes without speaking to or touching any of the children. Solomon ordered the boys and girls to wash their hands in basins of water. The girls turned up their long sleeves, the boys did not. One is reminded of how Huckleberry Finn's female disguise was penetrated when a piece of lead was tossed into his lap. Instinctively, he closed his knees to catch the weight rather than move his legs wider apart. (He also threaded a needle the wrong way, and threw the piece of lead the way a boy does.)

Another legend tells how the queen presented Solomon with two bouquets of flowers, one real, one artificial, and asked him to tell which was which without touching or smelling the blossoms. Can you guess how Solomon solved this problem? An answer appears in the First Answers section.

36 THANG, THE PLANET EATER

The first story I ever had printed was a short-short fantasy about a hyperbeing called Thang, presumably living in a fourth dimension. [The story has been reprinted in several anthologies, most recently in my *No-Sided Professor and Other Tales of Fantasy, Humor, Mystery, and Philosophy* (Prometheus Books, 1987).] He liked to reach into the Milky

36

Way galaxy to pick up planets and eat them the way we eat apples. Perhaps a better analogy, because Thang is four-dimensional, would be the way we eat extremely thin pancakes.

Imagine that Thang found a solar system to his liking, and that it took him seven days to eat all the planets. On the first day he ate 1/7 of the planets. On the second day he ate 1/6 of the remaining planets. On the third day he ate 1/5, on the fourth day he ate 1/4, on the fifth day he ate 1/3, on the sixth he ate 1/2. On the seventh day he ate the single planet left. How many planets were in the solar system?

This is easy to answer. There were seven. Thang simply ate one planet per day.

Let's complicate matters. Thang found another solar system to eat. This time he reversed his previous procedure. On the first day he ate one planet. On the second day he ate half the remaining number of planets. On the third day he ate 1/3, and so on to the seventh day when he ate 1/7 of the planets not yet eaten. A certain number of whole planets remained.

Your problem is this. What is the *smallest* number of planets the solar system can have that will allow this scenario? See the First Answers section.

FIRST ANSWERS

1 RIDDLES OF THE SPHINX

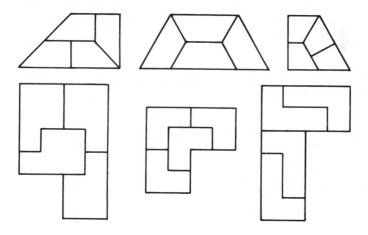

The figure above shows how the rep-tiles divide.

For almost a year Matsu tried to construct a pentagonal (five-sided) rep-tile, but without success. Then one day his associate Dr. Beatrice Mince, who had moved from Philadelphia to Tokyo to study Matsu's revolutionary techniques, managed to create the pentagonal rep-tile shown on the next page.

"Beautiful! Beautiful!," exclaimed Matsu, as he and Mince watched the highly magnified image of the organism wander about on the microscope's display screen. "What shall we call it?"

"How about *sphinx* " said Mince. "It has a shape that looks like a profile of the ancient Egyptian statue that once stood near the Great Pyramid."

"Ah, so," said Matsu. "You are right. What a pity the Sphinx was destroyed in the great Middle-East war of 2019."

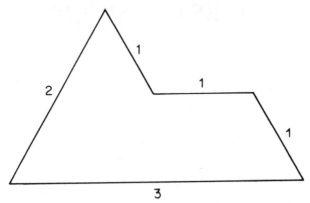

See if you can divide the inscrutable rep-tile into four smaller congruent sphinxes before you turn to the Second Answers section.

2 PRECOGNITION AND THE MYSTIC SEVEN

I predict your answer will consist of a 1, a 2, a 4, a 5, a 7, and an 8 in some order. It will contain no 6's, 3's, or 9's. How do I know this? Well, I could have simply tried all the possibilities, but there is a less tedious way to see why this works. By following the instructions, we obtain

$$\frac{1}{7} \cdot 999999 \cdot d = \frac{d}{7}(10^6 - 1) = \frac{d}{7} \cdot 10^6 - \frac{d}{7},$$

where d is the digit the die turned up. The division $1/7$ yields $0.\overline{142857}$ (the bar indicates that the sequence of digits under it keeps repeating). We observe that all six possible nonzero remainders occur in this division. The sixth remainder is 1 and from then on the remainders and the digits repeat.

Now the division $2/7$ consists of the arithmetic steps we performed after we reached the remainder 2 in the computation of $1/7$. That was the second remainder, so we get $2/7 = 0.\overline{285714}$. We have the same digits as above, in the same order, except that the sequence starts with the 2 instead of the 1. Similarly for $3/7, \ldots, 6/7$.

Clearly then, $1000000/7 = 142857.14285714\ldots$; and subtracting $1/7$ from this, which is represented by the sequence of digits behind the decimal point, we get $999999/7 = 142857$. Using our observations about $2/7, \ldots, 6/7$ above, we conclude that $2 \times 999999/7$, etc. are represented by cyclic permutations of 142857. We even know which cyclic permutation; $i/7$ is the one that starts with the ith smallest of the six digits.

Observe that we were asked to prove only that each of the digits $1, 2, 4, 5, 7, 8$ occurs exactly once in our six digit answer, but we derived much more detailed information about it. Note that someone asked to prove this more precise theorem would probably have found this easier than proving the weaker one we were given, because the stronger statement gives more of a hint of what is behind it, namely a single periodic decimal.

142857 is a positive integer whose six smallest multiples (including the number itself) are represented by cyclic permutation of its digits. Clearly there is no integer whose ten smallest multiples have this property, unless you allow a 0 in front. There are numbers whose 9 smallest multiples are cyclic permutations of the digits but finding them requires an effort, although it is not too difficult with a programmable calculator or computer. Can you find one? Look at the next answers section.

Seven was a popular symbol of divine perfection in medieval numerology. About twenty years ago Alan Cyril Bates of Chicago sent me the following limerick he had written about 777, which has the three prime factors 3, 7 and 37.

> Seven hundred seventy-seven
> Has 3 digits, each being 7.
>   Its factors are 3,
>   Also 7, you see,
> And a prime writ with 3 and a 7.

Now try this one. It involves the seven digits of your telephone number. On a sheet of paper, scramble the digits of your phone number to make a different seven-digit number. Put the larger of the two numbers in your calculator, and subtract the smaller one. Now subtract 2 and divide the result by 9. There should be a decimal remainder. Turn to the Second Answers section and I'll tell you more about that remainder.

3 ON TO CHARMIAN

1. If the digits are arranged 321654987 (or the reverse of this), the arrangement contains no subsequence of four digits in ascending or descending order. Remember, the four numbers need not be neighboring. They can be scattered through the sequence. If you are interested in a way

to prove the general theorem, and in references to some literature on it, see My Mathematical Magic Show, Chapter 15.

2. Since there are 84 ways to number the planets so that no four form a monotonic subsequence, the answer is 85.

The Erdös Szekeres theorem suggests a pleasant card game. Two players alternately select a card from a set of ten cards with values 1 through 10. The chosen cards are placed in a row in the order they are chosen. The first to play a card that completes a set of four in monotonic sequence wins. For example, if the first player, call him A, takes the ace, the second player (B) is sure to win if he takes a two. A is forced to take the ten. B takes the nine. Now no matter what card A takes next, B can complete a four-card monotonic subsequence on his next play.

The game can also be played in reverse form: the first to complete a four-card monotonic subsequence loses. No play in the standard or reverse version can end in a draw. The analysis of games involving the completion of monotonic sequences is not yet complete, although some results, which we will come to later, are known.

Back to the planets. On the day you first read this sentence, what planet was closest to you? See the Second Answers section for the answer.

4 TECHNOLOGY ON VZIGS

The memo describes life on Earth at some time not long before the twentieth century. The modular building units are of course bricks, and planks of wood held together by nails. Clothes are washed on a washboard, dried on a clothesline. Food is kept cold in ice boxes. Mathematical calculations and symbol processing are performed with a pencil. The transportation vehicle is a horse. The circular objects are coins, the engravings are postage stamps. The two behavior patterns are smoking and sneezing.

Now for you word-play buffs, what sort of simple substitution cipher did I use in giving the names of the planet and its star? The answer is in the Second Answers section.

5 THE VALLEY OF LOST THINGS

For definiteness, suppose the cards are $1, 2, 3, 4, 5$, in this order from bottom to top at the beginning. Also, it is easier to perform and to speak about the trick if we use five corresponding cards of a suit of another color instead of tearing the cards in half.

Cutting the deck repeatedly leaves the cyclic order unchanged; in particular, there will be precisely 4 cards between any two cards with the same number. When we divide the packet in half, before we turn the right half face up, each half will have one of each number, and cards with equal numbers will be at equal heights.

It is easier to visualize what happens next if we imagine the right half pack not being turned face up. To simulate the operations as originally described, we have to change our procedures as follows. When we work on the right hand pack, we transfer the bottom card to the top instead of moving the top card to the bottom; and when we remove cards from the piles, we remove the bottom card from the right pile instead of the top card.

In this modified setup, as we observed, the two piles originally have cards with equal numbers at the same levels. [A number is said to be congruent ($\equiv$) to n modulo k if n is the remainder when the number is divided by k. For example $15 \equiv 3 \pmod{12}$.] For each letter in the keywords, either we raise the positions of the cards in the left pile by 1 $\pmod 5$ or we lower the positions of the cards in the right pile by 1 $\pmod 5$. We use the expression $\pmod 5$, perhaps a bit loosely, to indicate that a level which gets out of the range 0–4 when we increase or decrease it by 1 is modified by subtracting or adding 5 to bring it back into the range. Here the bottom card has level 0.

We see that after each move,

level of a card in left pile $-$ level of the same-numbered card in right pile

increases by 1 mod 5. After 9 moves, the difference is therefore 4 $\pmod 5$ and so the top card of the left pile has the same number as the bottom card of the right pile. After we remove these, we have piles of 4 cards each and cards with the same numbers are at the same levels. If we now perform 7 operations, or any number which is congruent to 3 mod 4, the top card on the left pile will again have the same number as the bottom one on the right, etc.

6

6 AROUND THE SOLAR SYSTEM

Note that the names on the gray cells spell with an odd number of letters and those on the white cells spell with an even number. Mathematicians say that the two sets of squares, along with their names, are of opposite parity. One has even parity, the other odd. Each time the dime moves to an adjacent cell it changes parity.

If you start the dime on any cell and move to spell the letters of the name on that cell, the coin is sure to end on a white cell. Because the dime has now acquired even parity, all gray cells must be unoccupied, so it is safe to request that a penny be placed on gray Venus.

From now on, at each step, the dime moves an odd number of times. It makes no difference whether it is moved seven times (or any other odd number), or moved to spell S-E-V-E-N, or any other word with an odd number of letters. If some spectator's first or last name has an odd number of letters, you can use his or her name for spelling. Every time the dime is moved, its parity alters. This allows you to direct that a penny be placed on a vacant cell of a parity opposite that of the dime. After eight steps, the only unoccupied cell will be the moon, with the dime resting on Pluto.

If you want to repeat the trick with a different final result, you'll have to work out a different set of instructions. With suitable instructions you can, of course, cause the dime to end on any of the shaded squares. Be careful, though, to eliminate the cells in such an order that the moving "spaceship" always has access to all the remaining unoccupied cells.

Now for a simple but tricky little problem that involves another kind of tour around the same matrix.

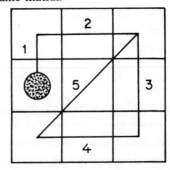

Place a dime on Mars. You are to move it in a sequence of straight line segments, each of which may be of any length and in a horizontal, vertical or diagonal direction. The task is to move the dime through all the remaining eight cells, and to do this with the smallest number of moves. For example, the figure on the facing page shows how it can be done in five moves. Incredible as it may seem, if you have the right "aha!" insight, you can do it in four. Most people find this task infuriatingly difficult, but don't spoil your pleasure in working on this clever combinatorial puzzle by looking at the answer in the Second Answers section before you have done your best to solve it. We must assume that the dime is actually a point, and that it passes over the center point of each cell.

7 THE STRIPE ON BARBERPOLIA

If you cut a right triangle out of paper, then roll it along its base to make a cylinder, you'll see that the hypotenuse will form a helix–a line that spirals around the cylinder from one end to the other.

Imagine that the cylinder shown on page 14 has been produced in this way. In your mind, unwrap the triangle, starting with corner A. The height of the right triangle corresponds to the cylinder's length. In this case, it is 14,400. Because the helical stripe goes seven times around the cylinder, the unwrapped triangle will have a base that is seven times the cylinder's circumference, or $7 \times 8,100 = 56,700$ km.

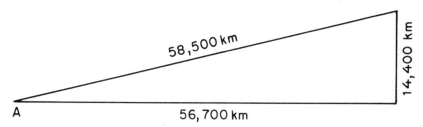

The helical stripe corresponds to the triangle's hypotenuse. Its square must equal the sum of the squares of the other two sides. The square of 14,400 is 207,360,000, and the square of 56,700 is 3,214,890,000. The sum is 3,422,250,000. A punch of your calculator's square root key gives the square root of this number as 58,500. This is the length in kilometers of the helical stripe.

As we all know, the cylinder is a popular shape for cans of food and drink. Shapes vary enormously, from tall thin cans to short fat ones. Suppose a manufacturer wanted to minimize the amount of metal needed for the entire surface (the lateral surface plus the two ends) of a can. In other words, he wanted the shape, given the can's volume, to make the surface area as small as possible.

There is a simple ratio between a cylinder's length and diameter that achieves this result. Do you know what it is? See Second Answers.

8 THE ROAD TO MANDALAY

1. The numeral 5 will appear 16 times. Did you forget it appears twice in 55?

2. The answer is 24. Not many people can count them all without drawing up a list.

3. Remove one nut from each of the other wheels and use them for the wheel you are changing.

4. After 10,000 km, each wheel has traveled that distance, making a total of 40,000 km for the four wheels. If five tires are used equally on the wheels, each tire has endured 40,000/5 or 8,000 km of wear.

5. A car following another car that never exceeds the speed limit can slow down, then easily exceed the speed limit in catching up.

6. Forty fence posts. Some people visualize the four corner posts, with eight posts in between on each side, for a total of 36.

7. Take a collection of coins amounting to more than a dollar which does not change a dollar. Attempt to make change for the dollar by counting out coins, always putting a coin of the largest value from the collection on the table until we exceed $1. The last coin we put down cannot be a half-dollar or a quarter, since we would have hit $1 exactly with those before exceeding it. It cannot be a nickel either, since we had at each stage an integer multiple of 5¢ on the table and cannot jump over one dollar by adding a nickel. Similarly the last coin put down is not a penny. So it must be a dime, and we must have $1.05 on the table. This must include an odd number of quarters. If the original collection contained a nickel or 5 pennies, they would still be available and could be used to replace the last dime, thus changing the dollar exactly. So our collection contained 1 or 3 quarters, no nickels and at most 4 pennies.

Now take out the odd quarter. The rest of the "silver" coins can be worth at most 90¢ since, by the above argument, we could change a dollar with it otherwise. 9 dimes is the largest number of coins we may have there, and we find that 1 quarter, 9 dimes and 4 pennies satisfies all our conditions.

8. One: a silver dollar. The next best answer is six: one half-dollar, one quarter, one dime, and three nickels.

"How about switching my memory to linguistics," suggested the car. "I'll give you a few word puzzles for a change."

"Good idea," I said, as I twiddled the dials.

1. "I'm a car, you're a man. Both *car* and *man* spell with three letters. I don't have many parts that are three-letter words—*fan*, for instance—but you have lots of them. Can you name ten parts of your body that spell with three letters?"

I couldn't get beyond nine.

2. We passed a sign that read: "Slow. Road Construction Ahead." Said the car: "Can you think of two words of *opposite* meaning, each of which can be put after the word *slow* to make a two-word sign, and in both cases the sign will say exactly the *same* thing?"

3. "I'm called the Hustle. There is just one way to rearrange those six letters of my name to make another familiar word. What is it?"

4. "*Continuum* has two adjacent U's. Give another common word with two adjacent U's. It's easy. In fact, there's nothing to it."

5. "What unusual word has three U's, not necessarily adjacent?"

6. What one-syllable word is immediately followed in the dictionary by the same word, with an additional letter at the end, that is three syllables?

7. What word completely changes its meaning if you capitalize it?

These questions are answered in the Second Answers section.

9 THE BLACK HOLE OF CAL CUTTER

Let's consider only a single face of each cube. The area of a face is the square of its edge, so the series of face areas is

$$\frac{1}{1} + \frac{1}{2} + \frac{1}{3} + \frac{1}{4} + \ldots + \frac{1}{n}.$$

Do you recognize this series? It is none other than the famous "harmonic series" that was the basis of a puzzle about bouncing superballs in Chapter 28 of *Puzzles from Other Worlds*. As is well known, the harmonic series *diverges*! This means that its partial sums increase without limit. The further you extend the series, the smaller each term becomes—in fact, they become as small as you please—nevertheless the sum slowly increases without an upper bound. There *is* no limit sum. The total area of Cutter's black hole is infinite!

There are many notorious examples in solid geometry of shapes with a finite volume and infinite surface area, but Cal's hole is one of the easiest to understand. Of course such a hole could not be painted inside with ordinary paint. You have to use an ideal paint of infinite thinness. After all, you are painting an infinitely thin surface.

What about the hole's depth? It, too, is infinite. How then could it have been constructed without allowing it to extend downward until it passed entirely through the earth? The answer is simple. After reaching a reasonable depth, Cal coiled the hole into a spiral. The coiling required is not simple. It cannot, for example, be coiled with the centers of each cube on a plane, nor can it be coiled by wrapping it around a cylinder or cone of finite size.

Speaking of black holes, I learned recently from Dennis Howard, who runs a science fiction bookstore in Asheville, NC, a startling fact. The term "black hole" was actually used by Edward Elmer ("Doc") Smith, the "father of space opera," in a novel he wrote several decades before physicist John Wheeler coined the term!

As all SF fans should know, Smith was a pioneer in writing pulp novels about spaceships that zoom around the universe, faster than light, carrying simple-minded men and beautiful women, all talking in the awful American slang of the early twentieth century. Smith's first space opera, *The Skylark of Space*, was written before 1920, but not published (in *Amazing Stories*) until 1928. In Chapter 12 the fiendish Marc DuQuesne has abducted Dorothy Vaneman, the hero's girl friend. His spaceship is struggling to escape the intense gravity field of what Smith calls a "dead star."

If you own a copy of this old pot boiler, see if you can locate the passage in Chapter 12 where the term "black holes" appears. If you can't find it, check the next answer section.

10 SCIENCE FANTASY QUIZ

1. The Earth, for one. Just toss the rock straight up.
2. The astronaut walked until he was certain he had gone farther than a kilometer. At some point along his path he has traveled *exactly* one kilometer.

3. As Victor Serebriakoff points out, in his *Mensa Puzzle Book* (1982), this ancient riddle does not specify that the eggs are chicken eggs. Because there were reptile eggs on earth long before there were chickens, eggs obviously came first.

4. Jorkens won the bet by reminding his friend that half a year ago the Earth was on the opposite side of the sun.

5. It is often claimed that the Great Wall of China is (as the *New York Times* put it on its editorial page of March 8, 1983) "the only mortal creation visible from the moon." It ain't so. No human-made structure on the earth is visible from the moon. Even the outlines of continents are hard to see.

6. It is a surprising consequence of the inverse square law of attraction that the force due to a homogeneous spherical shell is zero inside the cavity.

7. This would indeed work, and even supply a small amount of power. But it is no more a perpetual motion machine than devices that extract power from ocean tides. The gyroscope would be stealing power from the Earth's rotation, inevitably slowing the Earth's spin by a minuscule amount.

8. Rotate the page 90 degrees counter clockwise to see the name of the magazine.

9. Hold the page horizontally near the tip of your nose, close one eye, and read the message on a steep slant. (Thanks to Marvin Miller for this novel presentation of an old illusion.)

For a letter about Question 5, and my response, see the next answer section.

11 THE BARBERS OF BARBERPOLIA

The two barbers can complete the job in 22.5 minutes. Here's one way:

For the first 10 minutes the first barber cuts *A*'s hair, while the second barber shampoos *B* and *C*.

For the next 2.5 minutes the first barber cuts one-fourth of *B*'s hair, while the second barber completes the first half of shampooing *A*.

For the next 10 minutes the first barber cuts *C*'s hair, while the second barber finishes *A*'s shampoo, then during the remaining 7.5 minutes she completes *B*'s haircut.

Now for a slightly harder problem. It will introduce you to one of the most useful of all formulas in elementary algebra. As before, one barber completes a haircut in ten minutes. However, another barber, just learning the trade, takes twenty minutes. If the two barbers were allowed to work together on the same customer, how long would they take to cut his or her hair?

[See the Second Answers sections for this and other uses of the above-mentioned formula.]

12 IT'S ALL DONE WITH MIRRORS

If the *Bagel* had turned over an odd number of times in four-space, it would indeed have been reversed when it dropped back into the galaxy's three dimensions of space and one of time. VOZ knew this had not happened because if it had, the *Bagel* would have exploded the instant it landed!

Antimatter is reversed matter. If ordinary matter is mirror reflected, without altering its time direction, it becomes antimatter. As all SF fans should know, when matter and antimatter come together, both are totally annihilated. An object made of antimatter as large as the *Bagel*, landing on a planet of matter, would have caused an explosion far more powerful than any H-bomb. The entire mass of the ship, plus a comparable hunk of matter on the planet, would have been transformed entirely to energy.

Mirror-reflection symmetry plays an important role in modern physics and cosmology, including the grand unification theories designed to unify all the fundamental laws of the universe. As an entertaining introduction to mirror symmetry, try this mystifying experiment. It was invented and sent to me many years ago by Frank B. Brady.

Only one of the following five sentences is false. All the others are true:

1 CARSON WAS BORN CHRISTMAS DAY 1809—LIVED TO THE AGE OF 59

2 BUFFALO BILL WAS BORN IN 1846—HIS BIRTHPLACE WAS SCOTT COUNTY, IOWA

3 HICKOK DIED DEC 3 1883—DOC BEECH DECIDED HE CHOKED

4 CUSTER WAS KILLED AT LITTLE BIG HORN MONTANA IN JUNE 1876

5 CROCKETT OF TENNESSEE MET DEATH AT THE ALAMO IN THE YEAR 1836

A mirror will instantly identify the false sentence. Just hold these pages upside down in front of a mirror and look at the reflection. The false sentence will be the only one you can read!

Why should the glass reverse the four true sentences, and leave the false statement unaltered? The next answers section tells this and more.

14

13 SATAN AND THE APPLE

The story (the plot of which, by the way, I snitched from Lord Dunsany's Story "Told Under Oath" in *The Ghosts of The Heaviside Layer*) is not strictly contradictory, but it has a strong flavor of self-referential paradox. If the woman always tells the truth, then her last sentence must be true. But if it's true, her entire story, including the final sentence, must be false. On the other hand, if the last sentence is a lie, perhaps her story is true.

Many novels, short stories, and poems have played with similar themes of self-reference. You'll find some of the classics discussed in the chapter on logic paradoxes in my book *Order and Surprise*. My favorite example is a limerick, but to understand it you must first contemplate the following two-liner:

There was a young man from Peru
Whose limericks stopped on line two.

What do you make of this shorter limerick?

There was a young man from Verdun.

If you don't see (or hear) the paradox, check the next answer section.

14 HOW'S-THAT-AGAIN FLANAGAN

I leave it to readers to explain Flanagan's flimflam about the cube's space diagonals, and why balloons rise. The one-word anagram for CANOE is OCEAN.

Can you find a two-word anagram of CANOE that describes a familiar geometrical object? It is named in the Second Answers Section.

15 RELATIVISTICALLY SPEAKING

The reason a mammoth pair of scissors can't be used to send faster-than-light signals is this: When you wiggle the handles, the mechanical impulse has to go from molecule to molecule, and this transmission is slower than light. In relativity theory, material bodies are not absolutely rigid. Otherwise, you could send faster-than-light impulses by wiggling one end of a rod that extended an enormous distance. Unfortunately, the wiggle travels as a wave that moves slower than light.

Pulver was about to light his cigarette when Tanya, the daughter of the head of the *Bagel's* computer division, came over to the table. "Haven't you kicked the smoking habit yet?"

Pulver shook his head. "I've tried several times on this mission, but I can't seem to hold out."

"I know an easy way to quit."

"I'm all ears," said Pulver.

"There are fifty cigarettes in that pack, right?"

"Right."

"Here's what you do. After you finish the first one—the one you're about to light—wait one second before you light the next one. After the second cigarette, wait two seconds before you start another one. After the third, wait four seconds, then eight seconds on the next, and so on. Just keep doubling the seconds. I guarantee you'll never finish the pack."

"Is that so? Why not?"

"Figure it out," said Tanya.

Pulver made some quick calculations on his computer wrist watch. He was astounded. How long would he have to wait between his 49th and his 50th cigarette? A surprisingly long time (see the Second Answers section).

16 BAR BETS ON THE BAGEL

Both Flarp and Pulver failed to solve the problem. When Couth showed how to move the two matches, Pulver guffawed and slapped his forehead. "Amazing!" he exclaimed. "Why didn't *I* think of it?"

"Because you're stupid," said Flarp, "that's why."

Pulver was unoffended. He stared intently at the pattern on the table. "I can't believe it," he said at last, "but I think I've discovered a way to solve the problem by moving just *one* match."

"In words of one syllable," snorted Flarp, "impossible."

"Don't be too sure," said Pulver, wagging a finger in front of Flarp's nose. "Will you buy my next drink if I'm wrong?"

"It's a deal," said Flarp.

What in the name of Asimov does Pulver have in mind? You can find out in the Second Answers section.

17 CATCH THE BEM

The Evenoder will never catch the monster unless it first alters the game's parity. If a mathematical structure has two distinct states, one of which can be identified with even numbers, the other with odd numbers, the two states are said to be of opposite parity. In number theory, all even numbers have one kind of parity, and all odd numbers have the opposite parity. Some of the most famous proofs in number theory, for example a proof that the square root of 2 is irrational, are based on parity considerations.

In our game, the two states are distinguished as follows: If the Evenoder, when it is his turn to move, is separated from the BEM by an even number of horizontal or vertical blocks, the position has even parity. If he is separated by an odd number of such blocks, the position has odd parity.

The Evenoder cannot catch the BEM as long as the game's initial parity is conserved—that is, as long as he has an even number of vertical or horizontal blocks to go to reach the BEM, and the BEM stays away from the upper left hand corner. If the Evenoder can alter the parity, he can easily trap the BEM in one of the three right-angle corners.

There is only one way to alter the parity. He must head directly for the triangular block in the upper left corner and go around it. Once he does this, the BEM is easy to capture.

Parity considerations such as this arise in many board games. In checkers and chess, for instance, especially near the end of a game, a position's parity may determine who wins or loses. In particle physics, parity is identified with right and left mirror images. In 1957 C. N. Yang and T. D. Lee were given the Nobel Prize for discovering that in certain particle interactions mirror-reflection parity is not conserved.

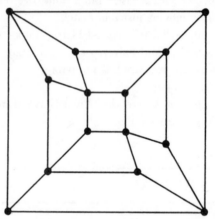

14 Towns on Evenod

Here is another problem based on parity. This figure shows a network of roads connecting 14 towns on Evenod. Is it possible to start at one town and follow a path that visits each town once and only once? In graph theory such a path is called a Hamiltonian path. (If such a path closes at the ends it is called a Hamiltonian circuit.) There is a delightfully simple way, using a "parity check," to prove that the network has no Hamiltonian path. The proof is given in the Second Answers section.

18 ANIMAL TTT

To win Tippy TTT first take the center cell. Thereafter always play directly opposite your opponent's last move. You won't win until you take the last cell, but that move will always form Tippy. (Of course if your opponent makes an error, and you see a chance to win on your next move, you can shorten the game.)

How about the other four-cell animals? The smallest boards on which Elly, Knobby, and Skinny are wins (for the first player; the second player can never win, as explained below), have orders 4, 5, and 7, respectively. Fatty, surprisingly, is a tie on all boards. The proof of this is very pretty, and will be given in the first chapter of a fascinating book Harary is writing on what he calls achievement and avoidance games.

Notice that in all the achievement games so far mentioned, the first player can always avoid losing. There is an amusing proof that in games of this type the second player cannot have a winning strategy. Assume there is a second-player winning strategy. The first player can make an arbitrary first move, then pretend he is the second player and steal the second player's strategy! His arbitrary first move cannot be a liability. If the strategy requires that he play on *that* cell, he simply makes another arbitrary move. We have now bumped into a contradiction. If the second player has a winning strategy, the first player can steal it and win! Of course the proof tells you nothing about *how* the first player can force a win or draw.

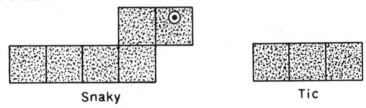

Snaky   Tic

There are many unsolved problems involving animal TTT. Consider Snaky, the six-cell animal shown above. Is she a winner for the first player, and if so, what is the smallest board on which she wins? Harary offers a $50 reward for the first proof, before 1990, that there is a board on which Snaky wins, and $100 for the first proof that she is never a winner.

Each of the above games has a variant in which both players make the *same* mark, say Xs, and the first to create the specified animal wins. Harary calls them one-color games. Ties obviously are not possible if the board is large enough to contain the animal. You might think that one-color TTT games are trivial. Far from it!

Consider Tic, the simple animal made of three cells in a straight line. It is easy to see that the first player wins if one-color Tic achievement is played on the order-3 board. The order-4 board is not easy to analyze and the outcome on an order-5 board is still unknown for the avoidance game.

Each of the four-cell animals will tile a square except for Tippy, who cannot tile any rectangle. Elly will tile a square if and only if its side is a multiple of four, and a rectangle if and only if the product of its sides is a multiple of eight and both sides are at least 2. As a pleasant task, which will not be answered because you will soon solve it, cut out six replicas of Elly and see how quickly you can form them into a 3×8 rectangle.

Together the five four-cell creatures have a total of 20 cells. Will the set tile a 4×5 rectangle? The answer is no, but can you prove it? The proof will introduce you to a powerful method based on a coloring technique; see the Second Answers section.

19 PLAYING SAFE ON THE BAGEL

The word is NTH (pronounced enth).

Tanya, who enjoyed every type of word play, spent many hours studying the safe's pattern of letters. The longest word she could find that uses only white letters was SEMISUCCESSES. PHFFFT was the longest expression she could find on the gray keys.

One afternoon Tanya covered the L key with a piece of blue tape. The Captain had eliminated all red tape on the *Bagel* by the simple expedient of allowing only blue tape.

"I've invented a new kind of puzzle," she said to her father. "What man's name does this keyboard signify?"

"That's easy," said Couth. "I'm afraid you reinvented an old chestnut. The answer is NOEL–no L. It's in one of Gardner's math books. Persons used to put it on Christmas cards back in the days when there was a popular Christmas carol that began with 'Noel, noel...' Don't look so disappointed. It was clever of you to think of it. Here's a similar one I remember seeing in an old British puzzle book."

Couth transferred the piece of blue tape from L to W.

Tanya studied the keyboard for several minutes. "How about a hint? What kind of word is it?"

"Let's say it describes where you can go on Earth and be absolutely safe during an all-out nuclear war."

Tanya never solved it. If you can't, turn to the Second Answers section.

20 SEX AMONG THE POLYOMANS

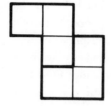

The missing shape is shown above.

In addition to his 3-cell animals, Dr. Matsu also constructed poly-omans with orders as high as 25. (The order of a polyomino is the number of cells it contains.) Some of the animals with five or more cells, he discovered, on rare occasions conjugate in triplets, quadruplets, and even quintuplets.

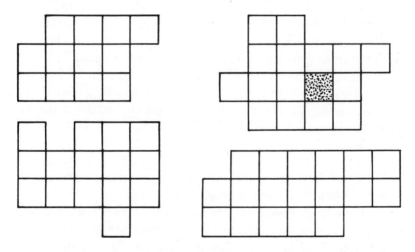

At the top of the figure, on the left, is a 12-cell animal formed by a pair of conjugating 6-cell creatures. Can you divide this shape into two identical 6-cell animals? On the right of this shape is a 15-cell animal formed by a triplet of conjugating 5-cell creatures. Note the interior hole. Can you cut this shape into three identical 5-cell animals?

At the bottom of the same illustration, on the left, is another 15-cell creature that you are asked to divide into three identical 5-cell animals. On the right is an 18-cell animal to be cut into three identical 6-cell poly-omans. These divisions are shown in the Second Answers section.

21 INNER PLANETS QUIZ

1. Until 1965 astronomers believed that Mercury's rotation period was exactly the same as its period of revolution around the sun. If true, Mercury would keep one hemisphere permanently facing the sun, just as our Moon keeps one face always toward the Earth. "Mercury has the distinction," the British astronomer Fred Hoyle wrote as late as 1962, "of possessing not only the hottest place but also the coldest place in the whole planetary system."

Using radar reflections from opposite sides of Mercury, astronomers discovered in 1965 that Mercury and the sun are in a stable 3-to-2 resonance lock. The little planet turns three times during every two orbits. There *is* no twilight zone.

2. Until recently many astronomers believed that Venus, like Mercury, also kept one face forever toward the sun. This too was accepted by many science fiction writers. "For Venus, of course, has no rotation," wrote Stanley G. Weinbaum in *The Lotus Eaters*, "and hence no alternate days and nights. One face is forever sunlit, and one forever dark, and only the planet's libration gives the twilight some semblance of season."

Radar measurements in 1962 revealed two amazing facts. Venus spins backward with respect to all the other planets of the solar system. (Uranus has an ambiguous spin direction; its axis is so nearly parallel with the plane of the ecliptic that either pole can be called north.) On Venus the sun rises in the west.

Venus orbits the Sun in 224.7 Earth days. Incredible as it may seem, the radar measurements of 1962 showed that the planet's spin period is about 243 Earth days, which is longer than its year.

3. If the Earth were reduced to the size of a billiard ball, it would not be as smooth as an ivory ball; it would be more like the outside of an orange. You would be able to feel the roughness of its surface. If the Earth's orbit were drawn to scale on a small sheet of paper, it would be impossible to distinguish it from a circle. The path is indeed an ellipse, but its deviation from the circle is too small to be noticeable.

4. Each end of the green side of a dollar bill can be pleated as shown in the figure on the facing page to show the face of a Martian. This suggests an amusing puzzle to spring on friends. How many eyes are on a dollar bill? Everybody counts the two eyes of Washington and the big eye at the top of the pyramid. The less obvious eye on the eagle makes four. That's as far as most people go. No, you insist, there are eight eyes. Pleat the bill at the two ends to prove it.

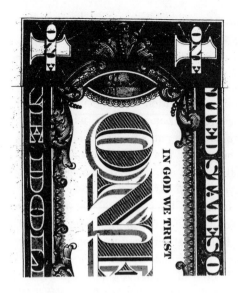

Now for four more questions about the same planets.

5. Does Mercury have a magnetic field?

6. Consider a moment when Venus is closest to Earth. (This situation is called "inferior conjunction"; we shall just call it "conjunction" from now on.) Under the assumption that the orbits of the two planets are circular and in the same plane, this would mean that Venus is on the line segment from the Earth to the Sun. The questions are

a) How many Earth days will elapse until the next conjunction?

b) How many times will Venus appear to have rotated around its axis to an observer on Earth who is constantly viewing the surface of Venus on a radarscope, and who perceives the changing image as if it were due solely to rotation of Venus around its own axis (although it is partly due to the fact that they both circle the sun and in the process the Earth goes around Venus). Think of Venus as a balloon with 10 red stripes going from one pole to the other, so that we can count rotations by counting the number of stripes that pass our view. We may regard Venus's axis of rotation as perpendicular to the plane of its orbit.

The answer to 6(b) is surprising; see the Second Answers section.

7. Everybody knows that the Moon's gravity causes the Earth's seas to rise on the side facing the Moon. Why is there simultaneously a high tide on the opposite side of the Earth?

8. You meet a lady who claims she comes from Mars. Indeed, she tells you, she was born there. Could she be telling the truth?

The questions are answered in the Second Answers section.

22 PUZZLES IN FLATLAND

The 15 moves are CEFDBACEGFDBCED.

Generalizations and variations of this classic puzzle lead into fascinating regions of algebra and combinatorics, where lovely symmetries are encountered. Here are some paths to explore:

1. Assume the puzzle has n black counters at one end, n white counters at the other, with one empty space separating them. Prove that the minimum-move solution has $n(n + 2)$ moves.

2. Below each letter of the solution above put S if the move is a slide, J if it is a jump. You get the string $SJSJJSJJJSJJSJS$. Note that the sequence is a palindrome. Prove that all minimum-move solutions for a board of length $n + 1$ have a palindromic sequence of slides and jumps.

3. Below each letter of the above solution put B for black and W for white. You get the string $BWWBBBWWWBBBWWB$, another palindrome. Show that all minimum-move strings are palindromes.

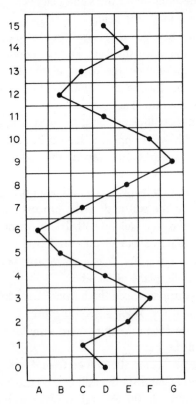

4. The figure on the facing page is a graph showing the movement of the blank cell in the minimum-move solution for $n = 3$. Observe that it has 180-degree rotational symmetry (looks the same upside down). Prove this true of all minimum-move solutions.

5. Analyze the puzzle when there are more empty cells than one between the two sets of counters.

6. Suppose the counters in the two sets are *not* equal: m black counters and n white with one vacant cell between them. Show that the minimum-move solution is of length $mn + m + n$, of which mn are jumps and $m + n$ are slides. Our original problem is, of course, a special case of this more general problem. Let $m = n$ and you get the formula $n(n + 2)$.

If we redefine the word "move," there is a joke solution to the original problem that lowers the number of moves from 15 to 1. If you can't think of it, turn to the Second Answers section.

---

23 DIRAC'S SCISSORS

Assume you twisted the scissors 720 degrees clockwise, as viewed from the ceiling. Hold the scissors in your right hand. With your left hand take the center of the twisted strands, carry the string up on the far side of the scissors, pass the loop over the scissors and allow it to fall on your right arm. Take the scissors in your left hand. Release the scissors with your right hand, allowing the loop of string to fall. Raise the scissors. You are back where you started. The tangles have vanished!

You don't have to have a pair of scissors to demonstrate the puzzle. Any object will do, and any number of strings can be attached to it provided there are more than two. The free ends may be fastened to any spots in the room. Imagine, for example, a coffee pot with a dozen elastic strings that run from the pot to any places on any wall or on the ceiling or floor. Rotate the pot 360 degrees around any axis. No manipulation of the elastic cords will restore the original structure. Rotate the pot 720 degrees and the restoration is always possible.

A variant of the experiment which, to some, may make it clearer how one can rotate an object connected to a wall by a cable or hose continuously without twisting the cable until it breaks is the following. It also makes clear that this most interesting observation was really familiar to everyone who ever wound or unwound a reel of hose or electrical wire and struggled with its twisting.

Take a full roll of toilet paper. Put the end of the paper under a heavy book on a table and move some distance from the table, with the roll in your hand. Face the table and hold the roll in a horizontal position, so that the strip to the table is not twisted. Insert two fingers of your right hand into the hole from the right and hold the roll with them. Loosen one complete turn of paper and pull it off the roll with your left hand without tearing it and without turning the roll. The strip will now be twisted. Repeat the operation with the roles of the hands reversed. Lifting off the second turn to the right imparts a reverse twist to the strip so that in the end the strip is longer and untwisted. Up to now we have not turned the roll. Now we are able to turn the roll two full turns about its axis, rolling back up what was taken off, and we get back to the original position. By repeating this process, we can rotate the roll as many times as we like without tearing the paper.

We want to explain how these experiments relate to "the property of rotations that two (complete) rotations of a body about an axis can be continuously deformed through a set of motions *which each end up with the original position* into no motion at all." (See Dirac's letter on page 47.)

The pieces of toilet paper which always stay on the roll undergo two full rotations in our experiment. Pieces farther out undergo other motions but each returns to its original position at the end of the experiment. Also, the motion of each is very close to that of neighboring pieces if we think of small pieces. If we go out along the strip until we reach the paper under the book, we find the series of motions mentioned by Dirac, ending with no motion.

Since the rotation is about an axis perpendicular to the direction of the strip, the experiment seems highly unsurprising, but of course the initial direction of the strip is immaterial; our paper could extend beyond the table and we could glue it to a point on the wall which is on the axis of rotation of the roll.

Dirac's strings model what topologists call "fiber bundles." If you care to learn more about how Dirac's scissors trick ties into fiber bundles and quantum mechanics, check "Fiber Bundles and Quantum Theory," by Herbert J. Bernstein and Anthony V. Phillips in *Scientific American*, July 1981, and letters on the article in the following October and December issues. See also the Amateur Scientist department of the same magazine, December 1975, for a description of a practical application of Dirac's scissors to an ingenious mechanical device that allows a cable to be rotated continuously without twisting it. Other good references include "The Spinor Spannor," by Ethan D. Bolker, *American Mathematical Monthly*,

November 1973, and "On a String Problem of Dirac," by M. H. A. Newman, in the *Journal of the London Mathematical Society*, July 1942.

There are endless anecdotes about Dirac. The best known involves the sister of Eugene Wigner, a Nobel prize-winning physicist. Shortly after Dirac married Wigner's sister, he was entertaining an old friend who had not yet heard of Dirac's marriage. I'll let George Gamow finish the story, as he tells it in *Thirty Years that Shook Physics*. The friend "found with Dirac an attractive woman who served tea and then sat down comfortably on a sofa.... 'Oh,' exclaimed Dirac. 'I forgot to introduce you. This is Wigner's sister.' "

Gamow reports another occasion on which Dirac was visiting Peter Kapitza, the famous Russian physicist. Dirac became absorbed in watching Mrs. Kapitza knit. A few hours after his visit he rushed back to the house to tell Mrs. Kapitza he had been thinking about the topological aspects of her knitting, and had discovered a second way to do it. After he showed her the second method, Mrs. Kapitza informed him that he had reinvented purling.

Our final story, again from Gamow, concerns the question and answer period following one of Dirac's lectures. Someone stood up to say, "I don't understand how you derived that formula on the left side of the blackboard."

Can you guess how Dirac replied? His response is in the Second Answers section.

24 BULL'S-EYES AND PRATFALLS

1. Lucretius, *De Rerum Natura* (On the Nature of Things), circa 99 B.C. This accurate description of evaporation shows that ancient Greek and Roman particle theory had more empirical support than some historians of science like to admit.

2. Roger Joseph Boscovich, *Theoria Philosophiae Naturalis* (Theory of Natural Philosophy), 1758. In today's particle theory, matter is believed to be made of six kinds of leptons and six kinds of quarks, all pointlike, with no internal structure.

3. Jonathan Swift, "A Voyage to Laputa," in *Gulliver's Travels*, 1726. Mars's two moons were not discovered until 1877. Phobos, the innermost moon, revolves in a trifle more than seven hours, and Deimos, the outermost moon, in about 31 hours. That Mars had two moons had earlier been predicted by Kepler. This was probably the basis of Swift's account.

4. Samuel Johnson, in a letter to Mrs. Thrale, November 12, 1791.

5. Robert Hooke, British physicist, in *Micrographia*, 1664.

6. Benjamin Franklin, in a letter to Abbé Soulavie, September 22, 1782.

7. Erasmus Darwin, Darwin's grandfather, in *Zoonomia*, 1794.

8. Alfred Tennyson, *Locksley Hall*, 1886.

Now see if you can name the single scientist responsible for the following pratfalls:

"The talking motion picture will not supplant the regular silent motion picture . . . . There is such a tremendous investment to pantomime pictures that it would be absurd to disturb it." (1913)

"It is apparent to me that the possibilities of the aeroplane, which two or three years ago was thought to hold the solution to the [flying machine] problem, have been exhausted, and that we must turn elsewhere." (1895)

"In fifteen years, more electricity will be sold for electric vehicles than for light." (1910)

"There is no plea which will justify the use of high-tension and alternating currents, whether in a scientific or a commercial sense . . . . My personal desire would be to prohibit entirely the use of alternating currents. They are unnecessary as they are dangerous." (1889)

The source of these is given in the next answers section.

---

25 FLARP FLIPS ANOTHER FIVER

"Suppose the odds favor an even number of heads," Tanya explained. "Obviously the same could be said of an even number of tails, because a head is as likely on any flip as tails. There's no way the odds can favor *both*, so the assumption that the odds favor both must be false. And the only way it can be false is if the probability of an even number of heads exactly equals the probability of an even number of tails."

Even Flarp was surprised by the simplicity of Tanya's reasoning. He started to toss the fiver, but Tanya stopped him with a hand on his arm.

"Don't be a male chauvinist," she said. "I have as much right to play as either of you two. Let's flip for a three-way decision."

"How can we do that?" Asked Flarp. "I have only one coin, and Pulver tells me he has only bills."

"*I* have some change," said Tanya, "but you really don't need more than one coin."

Again, what in space does Tanya have in mind? How can a single coin be used to decide fairly between three persons? See the Second Answers section for a solution.

26 BLUES IN THE NIGHT

The pink lady's reasoning seems intuitively correct, but it is quite wrong. The background information *is* essential in estimating the chances that the man was a blue.

I ran across this problem in *The Mind's New Science: A History of the Cognitive Revolution*, by Howard Gardner. The original problem involved the color of a taxicab as seen by a man with poor eyesight. Let's sharpen it by modeling it with an urn that contains 100 marbles. Fifteen marbles are green, 85 are blue. The marbles are randomly mixed, someone closes his eyes and draws a marble. He opens his eyes, notes the color, then replaces it in the urn. No one else is in the room at the time.

Later he says to a friend: "The marble I selected was green."

On the assumption that the man is accurate in distinguishing green from blue 4/5 of the time, what is the probability that the marble he selected was blue instead of green?

There are several ways to go about answering this question. One way is to draw the probability tree shown on page 102. The figures at the bottom show four percentages:

1. The percentage of times the man calls blue and the marble is blue is 68 percent.

2. The percentage of times the man calls green, and the marble is blue = 17 percent.

3. The percentage of times the man calls green, and the marble is green = 12 percent.

4. The percentage of times the man calls blue, and the marble is green = 3 percent.

These percentages, at the bottom of the inverted tree, are obtained by multiplying the values on the two line segments that connect each end of the branch with the urn at the top. The four percentages add, of course, to 100 percent.

We see that the man called a marble green .17 + .12, or 29 percent of the time. So the correct answer is that the probability the marble (or murder suspect) was blue is 17/29, or more than 1/2. A far cry from the pink lady's estimate of 1/5!

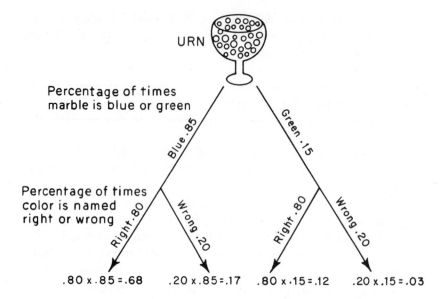

If you are doubtful about this answer, you may be able to convince yourself it is correct by the following more laborious procedure. Using *B* for a blue marble and *G* for green, list 85 *B*s and 15 *G*s on a sheet of paper. Circle 1/5 of the *B*s to indicate the number of times the man will incorrectly call a blue marble green. Circle 4/5 of the *G*s to indicate the times he will correctly call a marble green. There will be 29 circled numbers, indicating the 29 times the man said green. Count the number of *B*s in this set. You'll find there are 17. Therefore the probability the marble was blue is $17/29 = .586 +$.

In fairness to the pink lady I must add that L. Jonathan Cohen, a philosopher at Oxford University, has strongly defended her reasoning. He contends that in such a trial we are not dealing with a well-defined urn model in which it can be assumed that an experiment has been repeated hundreds of times. We have only the one-time case, and knowing that the person who named the color is wrong 1/5 of the time is all we need to know. The background information is irrelevant. The pink juror reasoned properly when she estimated the probability the man was blue at 1/5.

If you care to investigate Cohen's arguments you'll find them in his controversial paper "Can Human Irrationality Be Experimentally Demonstrated?" It's in *Behavior and Brain Science*, Volume 4, 1981. I side with the majority of statisticians who think Cohen is misguided, and that all he has done is show that few people have sufficient grasp of the subtle counterintuitive aspects of statistics to make good probability judgments.

Let's reduce the problem to absurdity. Suppose the man is right about the color just half the time. (Perhaps he flips a coin to decide whether to call blue or green.) If you had no background information about the ratio of blue to green marbles it would be rational to estimate the probability as 1/2 that the marble was blue when the man said green. But surely you would change your estimate if you knew the urn held a billion blue marbles to one green. And if you knew the urn contained *only* blue marbles, you would consider what the man said as totally irrelevant.

Not so fast! Let's defend Cohen's case. Our urn model assumes that the man who fled the scene of the crime was randomly selected from the city's mixed racial distribution, but we really don't know that. The woman may have had lots of boy friends, all or most of them green. Cohen's point is that situations like this, in real life, are too poorly defined, with too many unknown factors, to allow the application of formal reasoning. In any case, the problem has generated a great deal of sharp controversy. You'll find the most important papers listed in Gardner's (no relation) book.

27 AGAIN, HOW'S THAT AGAIN ?

Consider cell 2. It is impossible to give a two-move sequence that unambiguously puts the king there. $U\overline{U}$ is ambiguous because it could also put the king on 1 or 3. UL won't do because it could also put the king on 1. Try as you will, you'll not be able to specify an unambiguous two-move sequence that puts the king on any side cell or on the central cell. Therefore, *by definition*, those cells are undecidable. The person in the next room could move the king to any of these five cells, then speak truly!

What's going on here? Apparently we can prove that all nine cells are decidable, and also that five cells are not!

You may observe, however, that we sneakily altered the meaning of "undecidable" as we went along; the original definition required that we locate the king using no information other than two symbols, but then we slipped into transmitting the additional information that the cell is "undecidable."

The paradox is closely related to the more familiar paradox of the "unexpected hanging"—the basis of a chapter in my *Unexpected Hanging*, as well as Puzzle 20 in *Science Fiction Puzzle Tales*. This variant with the chess king was invented by Roy Sorensen, a philosopher at the

University of Delaware. He discusses it in his paper "Recalcitrant Variations of the Prediction Paradox," in *The Australian Journal of Philosophy*, Vol. 69, December 1982, pages 355–362.

As Flanagan said when he showed me the paradox: "It's the most unheard of thing I ever heard of."

28 ALICE IN BEELAND

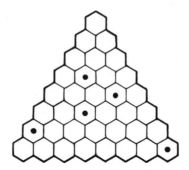

Five nonattacking bee-rooks can be placed on the order-8 triangle as shown above. Herbert Taylor, a California mathematician, has been investigating problems involving nonattacking bee-rooks on honeycomb fields of both triangular and hexagonal shapes, but has not yet published his interesting results. I can tell you, however, that the maximum number of nonattacking bee-rooks on triangles of sides 9 through 13 are 6, 7, 7, 8, and 9 respectively. See the Second Answers section.

The beeline problem

Before Alice left Beeland, Herbert showed her a variety of puzzles involving honeycomb triangles. Here, for example, is one that requires drawing a continuous path of beelines (straight-line segments) that go through the interiors of all the cells of an order-4 triangle. Herb showed Alice how it could be done with four beelines (left). After thinking about it for a while, Alice managed to do it with three (right).

"Would you bee-lieve it," said Herb, "it can be done with as few as *two* beelines?"

Two rules must be obeyed. Each cell is to be entered once and only once, and the lines must lie entirely within the triangle. For a solution and further questions, see the Second Answers section.

29 HUSTLE OFF TO BUFFALO

The states are Wyoming and Utah.

"Let me tell you about a remarkable numerical coincidence," I said to Hus. "The birth years of Washington, Lincoln, Franklin Roosevelt, and Reagan are respectively 1732, 1809, 1882, and 1911. Put them in a row. Under the first number write the difference between it and the second number. Under the second number put the difference between it and the third. Under the third put its difference from the fourth, and under the fourth, its difference from the first."

We are concerned only with absolute differences—differences that are positive. The procedure gives a new set of four numbers, like so:

1732	1809	1882	1911
77	73	29	179

Repeat the procedure as long as possible. The result is hard to believe:

77	73	29	179
4	44	150	102
40	106	48	98
66	58	50	58
8	8	8	8
0	0	0	0

"How extraordinary!" the car exclaimed. "May I have a few minutes to analyze it?"

"Fine by me, pal. Provided you keep your perceptrons on the road."

"Don't worry. I process in parallel, as you well know."

Is it a remarkable coincidence? See the Second Answers section.

30 RAY PALMER'S ARCADE

One experiment is to let two steel balls, held far apart, drop simultaneously. A careful measurement of their paths will show them to be parallel if the elevator is accelerating upward. If it is at rest on a planet, the paths will move closer together as each ball falls toward the planet's center.

Does this violate Einstein's famous principle of equivalence? No, but it *does* prove that the gravitational field surrounding a planet or star has a spherical structure that can't be duplicated by an elevator accelerating upward.

31 PUZZLE FLAGS ON MARS

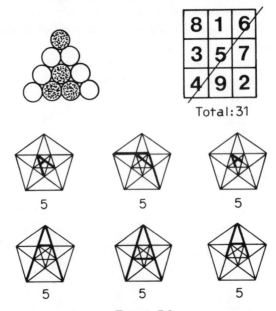

Total: 31

Total: 30

The illustration at the top left shows how the four circles are shaded. The solution is unique, not counting rotations. Note that two of the equilateral triangles that must be eliminated by the coloring are triangles that do not have a horizontal side.

The top right illustration shows how to draw a line on the *lo shu* to obtain the maximum total of 31.

To construct a 3×3 magic square with consecutive even numbers starting with 2, simply double the number in each cell of the *lo shu*. Now take 1 from each cell of this "even" magic square and you'll have the "odd" square containing the consecutive odd numbers starting with 1.

The magic constants of these squares are 30 and 27 respectively. The constant of any magic square, by the way, is easily determined. Simply add all the numbers in the square and divide by the number of horizontal rows (or vertical columns).

Once the *lo shu* was shown, it was easy to construct the even and odd versions; but how does one find expressions for appropriate entries into a 3×3 magic square? The makers of the *lo shu* flag may have hit upon it by trial and error; but perhaps you can think of a more systematic attack (before looking at the Second Answers section) by finding a relation between the entry in the center of the square and the "magic" constant.

The bottom illustration shows how to find six sets of the letter *A* to make a total of 30. The answer to the swastika problem is given below.

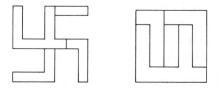

---

32 THE VANISHING PLANK

Although only half the plank has been removed, the plank has disappeared in the sense that no remaining piece has a length greater than zero! You can see this by considering the decreasing lengths of the segments that remain after each step. The first step leaves two segments of length 3/8. The segments get smaller and smaller after each step, their lengths approaching zero at the limit. In other words, after the Great Aleph has completed his task, no piece of the plank remains that has a length longer than zero. There is, therefore, nothing left to be seen. The plank has effectively vanished, even though half of its original substance is still there!

For a proof that part of the plank is still there, see the Second Answers section.

33   987654321

The nine questions of the number quiz are answered as follows:

9. The number 987654321 is divisible by 9, and therefore is a composite (nonprime). The fastest way to determine if a number is a multiple of 9 is to add all its digits, then add the digits in the sum, and continue until a single digit remains. The original number is a multiple of 9 if and only if this final digit (called the "digital root" of the number) is 9. The digits of 987654321 add to 45, and $4 + 5 = 9$, therefore the original number is divisible by 9. Of course this means it is also divisible by 3.

8. All factorials greater than 1! have 2 as a factor and therefore must be even. Moreover, all factorials greater than 5! must end in 0. Each criterion shows at once that 987654321 is not a factorial.

7. Any number divisible by an even number must end in an even digit. Since our giant number ends in 1, it cannot be a multiple of 2, 4, 6 or 8. It cannot be a multiple of 5 because all odd multiples of 5 end in 5.

Is it divisible by 7? Yes. The number 987,654,321,987,654,321 divides evenly by 7, therefore our giant number which consists of half a million repetitions of this multiple of 7 is also divisible by 7.

6. The fastest hand test of whether a large number is a multiple of 11 is to add all the digits in even positions, do the same for those in odd positions, and find the difference between the two sums. The original number is a multiple of 11 if and only if the difference is 0 or a multiple of 11. When we apply this test to 987654321987654321 the digits in even positions and those in odd positions each add to 45; the difference is 0. Hence the 18-digit number is a multiple of 11, and therefore our giant number is also.

5. If we divide 987654321987654321 by 987654321 the quotient obviously is 1000000001, therefore the giant number can also be divided by 1000000001. Since

$$1000000001 = 7 \times 11 \times 13 \times 19 \times 52579$$

(the number's prime factors) we know that our giant number also is a multiple of each of those factors. It is by using dodges like this that factors can often be found for enormous numbers without having to write complex computer programs.

4. It is shown in most introductory number theory books that even perfect numbers all have the form

(1) $(2^p - 1)2^{p-1}$, where $2^p - 1$ is prime.

In particular, an even perfect number must have exactly two different prime factors.

The prime factors of a perfect number have to satisfy various relations. If there are more than 2 prime factors it does not seem possible to satisfy them all, and most mathematicians think there are no perfect numbers other than the even ones of the form (1). There is no proof of this; but for a given odd number it is easy to show that it is not perfect, even if one can not factor it. If it has small factors, one quickly finds a condition which is not satisfied; if the number has only large factors, then the sum of its divisors will be much smaller than the number itself, and there is no need to utilize the more delicate relations mentioned above.

We know $N = 987654321$ is divisible by 9, and we find that 9 is the highest power of 3 that divides it. Let S be the sum of those divisors of N which are *not* multiples of 3. Then $3S$ will be the sum of all divisors which are multiples of 3 but not of 9, and $9S$ will be the sum of all the divisors which are multiples of 9. Hence the sum of all divisors, including N, is $(1 + 3 + 9)S$, and we want to show this is not $2N$. If it were, N would be divisible by 13, but when we perform the division, we find it is not.

As an example of a case when there is no small factor, we prove that $M = 8280485077$ is not perfect. We try out the primes < 17 and find none divides it. Let the factorization of M into prime powers be

(1) $M = p^a q^b \ldots .$

Since each factor is ≥ 17 and $17^9 > M$, there are at most 8 of them. The sum of all the divisors, including M, is

$$\sigma = \left(p^a + p^{a-1} + \cdots + 1\right)\left(q^b + q^{b-1} + \cdots + 1\right) \cdots$$

(2)

$$< p^a \frac{p}{p-1} q^b \frac{q}{q-1} \cdots \left(= M \frac{p}{p-1} \frac{q}{q-1} \cdots \right).$$

The inequality was obtained by replacing the finite geometric progressions by the corresponding infinite progressions, whose sums are given by simpler formulas.

If M were perfect, σ would be $2M$, and hence the product of the fractions in the second line of (2) would be > 2. However, since the prime factors $p, q, \ldots$ are all ≥ 17, we have

$$\frac{p}{p-1} = 1 + \frac{1}{p-1} \leq 1 + \frac{1}{17} < 1.06, \qquad \frac{q}{q-1} < 1.06, \ldots .$$

The product of at most 8 such factors is < 1.6. Therefore M is not perfect.

When an even perfect number, which we know has the form (1), is written in base 2, it has a simple pattern. It consists of p ones followed by $p-1$ zeros, and is perfect if and only if the number represented by the sequence of ones (in base 2, of course) is prime. For example, the first four perfect numbers are 6, 28, 496, and 8128. In the binary notation they are 110, 11100, 111110000, and 1111111000000. The primes represented by the ones are 3, 7, 31 and 127. It is easy to see that the number of ones must itself be a prime for a binary number consisting of ones to be a prime. Indeed, if the number of ones is divisible by, say, 3 then the binary number in question is divisible by 111. For instance, 111111111111 = 111 × 1001001001. In more conventional notation this statement is: $2^n - 1$ is a prime only if n is prime.

Can you think of a similar proof that the number $100\ldots01$ can be prime only if the number of digits, not counting the last, is a power of 2? See the Second Answers section.

The numbers $2^p - 1$ are called Mersenne numbers. The sequence of Mersenne numbers increases very rapidly. Testing them for primality by trying out all possible divisors is out of the question, even with a computer, except for the first few. However, Edouard Lucas invented a primality test for such numbers by which p's beyond 100 could be dealt with by hand. With computers, numbers with p of the order of 100,000 can be tested. The Mersenne prime $2^{21701} - 1$ was discovered by high school students Laura Nickel and Kurt Noll; he discovered also that $2^{23209} - 1$ is prime (in 1979). A program written by David Slowinski and run on the Cray supercomputer owned by Chevron Geosciences discovered that $2^{216091} - 1$ is prime. This is the 30th Mersenne prime discovered. Chevron's prime has 65,050 digits in decimal form and it is the largest prime known to the author at the time of writing; these days it does not take long until such a record is overtaken.

It is not known if there are infinitely many Mersenne primes. While the distribution of primes is irregular, among numbers of magnitude n, on the average, every $(\ln n)$-th number is prime, where ln denotes the natural logarithm. (The least precise forms of this very surprising statement are not even very difficult to prove but we have to refer you to textbooks on number theory.) If we make the assumption that $2^n - 1$ is as likely to be prime as a randomly chosen odd number of its size, then there should be infinitely many Mersenne primes. While this assumption is dubious, it predicts there should be about 36 Mersenne primes $< 300,000$ which is in the same ball park as the actual number, 30.

A fairly recent account of the computations involving perfect numbers and a proof of the Lucas test can be found in *Computational Methods in Number Theory* I, H. W. Lenstra Jr. and R. Tidjeman, editors. Centre Tract 154, Mathematisch Centrum, Amsterdam 1982. See also Carl Pomerance: *Notes on Primality Testing* (MAA Notes, 1984), and Daniel Shanks: *Solved and Unsolved Problems in Number Theory*, 3rd Ed. Chelsea, N.Y. 1985.

33

3. The unique solution is:

$$9 + 8 + 7 + 6 + 5 - 4 - 32 + 1 = 0$$

2. Here is a proof that no number starting with 9 and followed by digits in cyclic descending consecutive order (with or without 0 separating the repeated sequences) can be prime. All primes except 2 and 5 end in 1, 3, 7 or 9. In each of these cases, the sum of the digits in the number we are examining is a multiple of 3; hence the number is not a prime. Neither are those ending in 5 or in an even digit.

Primes *can* be generated if the digits are taken in ascending order. The smallest such prime is 1234567891. Only one other prime of this type is known. It consists of 123456789 repeated seven times and followed by 1234567. This mammoth number was conjectured to be a prime (with almost complete certainty) by Alan Cassel in 1977, and proved prime by R. E. Crandall and Michael A. Penk in 1978.

1. To arrange the cards for the spelling trick, simply perform the operations backward! Hold the ace in your left hand, put the deuce on top, then spell TWO by transferring three cards from bottom to top. Continue in this way with 3, 4, 5, 6, 7, 8 and 9. You will end with the packet properly arranged for performing the trick.

The method obviously applies to spelling any number of cards in any desired order. For instance, you can arrange all 52 cards so that you can spell and discard all of them in whatever sequence you like. Of course the cards need not be playing cards. They can be baseball cards, pictures of friends, or pictures of anything. You can always arrange the "deck" so you can perform the spelling trick with the names of whatever is on the cards.

Here are some amusing number stunts involving 987654321 that you can try on your calculator. Divide 987654321 by 123456789. The answer will surprise you. For another surprise divide 987654312 (note the reversal of 2 and 1) by 8. More surprises will follow if you add 123456789 to 987654321, or if you subtract the smaller from the larger. In the latter case, it is not obvious at first that all nine digits are in the difference. If 987654321 is multiplied by 2, 4, 5, 7 or 8, all ten digits appear in each product. If the multiplier is 2, the product has the five odd digits on the left, and five even digits on the right.

Now for a curious combinatorial puzzle involving the twelve numbers on the face of a clock. Can you rearrange the numbers (keeping them in a circle) so no triplet of adjacent numbers has a sum higher than 21? This is the smallest value that the highest sum of a triplet can have.

I know of no procedure for finding such a permutation, but there must be a way to write a computer program that will print all such permutations in a reasonable time. The Second Answers section confirms this much.

34 TIME-REVERSED WORLDS

"Consider what happens," said Ada, "if after you get the first reply on your Day 2, you erase the computer program you are supposed to send on your Day 100. You will have received an answer to a message never sent! A message is sent. The same message is *not* sent. A equals not-A. It's as sharp a logical contradiction as you can find in a theory."

One might counter that in MacBeath's scheme one simply doesn't permit erasing the message. Clearly that won't remove the flaw. A theory that allows a contradiction has to be abandoned. It's as if a logician invented a new formal system of logic, then someone discovered a chain of deductions that led to a statement being both true and false. It won't save the system to say: "We won't allow such a chain." If the system permits proving a statement to be both true and false, it is logically inconsistent. It has to be discarded or the flaw repaired.

The comic Henny Youngman has a joke about a man who tells his doctor: "My foot hurts when I move it like this." The doctor replies: "Don't move it like that." For years Einstein tried to think of experiments that would prove quantum mechanics is logically inconsistent. One famous argument was so subtle it kept Niels Bohr up all night trying to find the flaw in Einstein's reasoning. Ironically, it turned out that Einstein had forgotten to take into account the influence of relativity theory in his thought experiment!

Einstein failed to uncover a single logical inconsistency in quantum mechanics, though for the rest of his life he was convinced that the theory was incomplete. What he called "a little voice" told him that the theory would eventually be replaced by a deeper theory that would restore classical causality and rid quantum mechanics of its tendency toward solipsism. If the moon doesn't exist unless someone is looking at it, he liked to ask, will it exist if only a mouse looks at it?

For discussions of problems involving time reversal and time-reversed worlds, see the relevant chapters in my *Ambidextrous Universe*, and the references cited therein.

35 THE WISDOM OF SOLOMON

Solomon opened a window allowing bees to enter the palace room. The bees settled on the genuine blossoms.

The least known of all the legends about Sheba's visit, which I relate here with impeachable authority, concerns the whimsical way the Queen reacted when Solomon asked her to marry him. Her servants brought in two bowls. One contained ten gold talents, the other ten silver talents.

"After you are securely blindfolded," said Sheba, "I will move the bowls about the table at random. You will then select one of the bowls, and from it you will take a single talent. If it is gold, I will accept your proposal of marriage. If it is silver, I'll have to think about it."

Solomon meditated for several minutes, then said with a smile: "Oh Mighty Queen, may I be permitted to rearrange the talents in any manner I desire?"

Sheba pondered the question. With gold and silver divided evenly between the two bowls, Solomon's chance of drawing a gold talent obviously was 1/2. Suppose he mixed them so each bowl held five gold talents and five silver ones. The probability of selecting a gold talent would still be 1/2. Try as she would, the queen could see no objection to granting Solomon's request.

How did Solomon redistribute the 20 talents so that the probability of his taking a gold talent rose to almost 3/4? The surprising answer is in the Second Answers section.

36 THANG, THE PLANET EATER

36

The smallest number of planets that permits Thang's eating proce-dure is the lowest common multiple (LCM) of integers 1 through 7, with one planet added to be eaten on the first day. The LCM of the seven numbers is 420. Thus there were $420 + 1 = 421$ planets at the start. Thang ate them in the sequence 1, 210, 70, 35, 21, 14, 10. The total is 361. Taking this number from 421 we get 60, the number of planets left uneaten.

Our next problem is not harder, but certainly trickier and more confusing. Again, Thang found another solar system he liked. Again he feasted each day for a week. On the first day he ate half the planets plus half a planet. The second day he ate half the remaining planets plus half a planet. Each succeeding day he did exactly the same, eating half the planets left plus half a planet. After his seventh meal, all the planets were consumed. By "half the planets" we mean half the number of planets. In working on the problems here it is best to think of all the planets as having the same mass. Otherwise, eating "half the planets" might pose extremely uneven stresses on Thang's digestive system.

How many planets did the solar system have at the start? The solution is simple once you have the right insight; see the Second Answers section.

SECOND ANSWERS

1 RIDDLES OF THE SPHINX

The figure below shows how a sphinx replicates.

Note that the original sphinx faces left. We will call it an *L*-sphinx. Of the four smaller sphinxes, only one is an *L*-sphinx. The other three face right, and are called *R*-sphinxes.

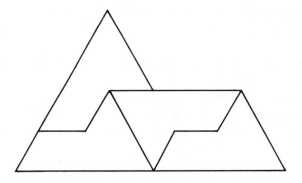

Exactly 24 hours after its birth, a sphinx reaches maturity, splits into four parts, then dies. Let's assume that a sphinx colony begins at noon, on day zero, with a pair of newborn sphinxes of opposite handedness, one left, one right. At noon on the first day there will be eight sphinxes, four left, four right. On the second day at noon there will be 32 sphinxes, 16 of each handedness; on the third day, 128 sphinxes, evenly divided between left and right forms. In other words, the population quadruples each day, always maintaining an equal number of right and left types. Of course the population is severely limited in growth by the amount of food available in the monolayer, otherwise sphinxes would soon blanket the Earth.

What happens if the colony starts on day zero with just one *L*-sphinx? On the first day there will be one left and three right forms. On the second day there will be ten left forms and six right. It is not hard to see that there is never equality in the numbers of left and right sphinxes. At each generation the majority shifts from one handedness to the other, the excess of one type always increasing, but at the same time growing steadily smaller in proportion to the total population. This suggests some fascinating problems in elementary combinatorics.

For an easy starter: How many sphinxes of each handedness will there be on the afternoon of the seventh day? For a systematic count, see the Third Answers section.

2 PRECOGNITION AND THE MYSTIC SEVEN

We are looking for a number whose 9 smallest multiples are cyclic permutations of the digits. From what we said in the First Answers section, it suffices to find a number such that

a) if you form its reciprocal by long division, the remainders $2, 3, 4, 5, 6, 7, 8, 9$ will all occur, and

b) nine times the reciprocal of the number has the same number of digits as the number itself.

The second condition is fulfilled for any integer with first digit 9. Using a computer one finds that the division $1/97$ yields all the above remainders and in fact all integers from 1 to 96 as remainders. From this we conclude that a number with the required property is

103092 783505 154639 175257 731958 762886 597938 144329
896907 216494 845360 824742 268041 237113 402061 855670;

the digits here constitute the first complete period of $10/97$.

The above sequence of digits has the following additional interesting property observed by Peter Ungar. All 2-digit sequences except 00, 33, 66 and 99 occur in it exactly once if we think of it as a cycle, i.e. 70 is followed by 10. Can you see a simple reason why this is so? See the Third Answers section.

The decimal remainder in the telephone number puzzle will be a stutter of 7s.

I'll explain this in part. If you rearrange the digits of any number to form a second number, and take the smaller from the larger, the result will always be a multiple of 9. You were told to subtract 2 from such a multiple. The result, therefore, is sure to be a number with a remainder of 7 when it is divided by 9. The fraction $7/9$ in decimal form is .777777 ... .

Our final trick is a truly astounding feat of precognition. Think of any word. Write it seven times on a sheet of paper. Fold the sheet in half and sit on it. Now turn to the Third Answers section. I'll not only tell you what's on the paper, but I'll also tell you where you got those shoes you are wearing.

3 ON TO CHARMIAN

The Earth, of course!

It was while the *Bagel* was making plans to explore the barren surface of Iras that it received an unexpected bulletin from home base. A newly-launched infrared satellite probe had just transmitted convincing evidence of an eleventh planet! It was promptly named Charmian because Iras and Charmian are the two faithful attendants of Cleopatra in Shakespeare's famous play. Some readers may recall that just before she died Cleopatra kissed them both, saying "Farewell, kind Charmian. Iras, long farewell." After the kiss, Iras dropped dead, either from a heart attack or because she, too, had allowed the asp to bite her.

Larc Snaag, the *Bagel's* captain, was a great admirer of Shakespeare. "Iras, farewell," he said over the intercom after canceling plans for a landing. "On to Charmian!"

Now see how quickly you can find a familiar English word that can be made by scrambling the letters of CHARMIAN.

4 TECHNOLOGY ON VZIGS

The cipher consists of interchanging A with Z, B with Y, C with X, and so on, taking the alphabet in reverse order. VZIGS decodes as EARTH, and HFM as SUN. Abraham Sinkov, in *Elementary Cryptanalysis*, reports that the U.S. Army actually made use of this cipher in the past. He points out that the cipher is equivalent to identifying the nth letter of the alphabet with the $(25n + 1)^{\text{st}}$ letter (modulo 26).

So far as I am aware, a totally unexplored region of word play is the finding of common words that translate, using this reverse alphabet cipher, into other familiar words. Indeed, I have been able to find only a few short examples—TOLD to GLOW, for instance. It might even be possible, though surely not easy, to construct sentences that translate into other sentences.

For some reader responses to my remark that the reverse alphabet cipher opened up new word-play possibilities, see the Third Answers section.

6 AROUND THE SOLAR SYSTEM

The figure below shows how the dime can tour the solar system in just four moves. Who said the coin couldn't slide outside the square?

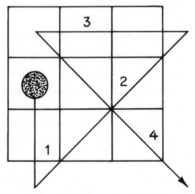

Let's relax the conditions even more. If it is required only that a portion of each cell be passed over by a portion of a moving dime (it need not start on the Mars cell), can the puzzle be solved in fewer than four moves? The Third Answers section has a reply.

7 THE STRIPE ON BARBERPOLIA

The shape of a right circular cylinder that minimizes its surface area, for a given volume, is a cylinder with a height exactly equal to its diameter. In a moment we shall show how this surprisingly simple result can be derived from an even simpler and unsurprising fact, but first we want to mention some of the reasons cans or barrels are seldom proportioned in this way.

The most obvious reason is that one wants to minimize cost, which is not the same as minimizing surface area. To achieve a prescribed strength, the mantle can often be made of a cheaper material than the top and the bottom; the length of the seams also enters into the cost. These considerations favor shapes which are taller than they are wide. The way a can looks may increase its sales, and taller cans appear to contain more than shorter cans of equal volume.

Now we relate the shape of a cylinder of least surface area for a given volume to the shape of the prism with a square base with the smallest surface area for a given volume. Since it is not at all surprising that the solution of the latter problem is a cube, the equality of the height and diameter of the minimal surface cylinder will also appear rather natural.

First we consider a configuration in the plane consisting of a circle C of radius r and a square S circumscribed about it. Let p_C, p_S denote the perimeters of the circle and the square. We have

$$(1) \qquad \text{area}\,(C) = \frac{r}{2}p_C, \qquad \text{area}\,(S) = \frac{r}{2}p_S,$$

as one can see by dissecting each of these figures into triangles with bases on the perimeter and tips at the center of the figure. (In the case of the circle one must think of numerous very narrow triangles.) All these triangles have height r. It follows that

$$\text{area}\,(C) : \text{area}\,(S) = p_C : p_S;$$

these ratios are both equal to $\pi : 4$ but that is not needed for our argument.

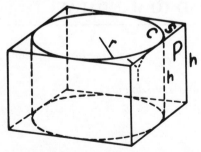

Now consider a circular cylinder Y of radius r and height h and a prism P with a square base circumscribed about it, (see Figure). In the top plane and the bottom plane we find the configurations described above; so the bases and hence the volumes of these prisms are in the ratio $p_C : p_S$. The areas of their mantles are also in this ratio, as one can see by unrolling them into rectangles. Hence

$$\frac{\text{surface area of } Y}{\text{surface area of } P} = \frac{\text{volume of } Y}{\text{volume of } P}.$$

Thus if we knew that among all prisms with a square base and some fixed volume the one with minimum surface areas is a cube then we could conclude that the cylinder inscribed into the cube has minimum surface area among all circular cylinders with the same volume.

The statement about the cube can very easily be proved using calculus, but then so can our original statement about the cylinder; so we present an alternative way which relies on the fact that the arithmetic mean of three positive numbers is greater than their geometric mean unless the three numbers are equal. (See *An Introduction to Inequalities*, by Edwin Beckenbach and Richard Bellman, NML vol. 3, p. 53.)

We minimize surface area among not just prisms with square bases but among arbitrary rectangular parallelopipeds with edges a, b, c. The surface area of such a solid is $2(ab + ac + bc)$. The product of the three terms in the parenthesis is V^2. Thus their geometric mean depends only on V, and hence their arithmetic mean, and their sum, is least if they are all equal. This is so only if the parallellopiped is a cube, q. e. d.

Suppose we want to make a box in the shape of a prism whose base is a regular hexagon. Can you figure out what the proportions should be to minimize the surface area for a given volume? See the Third Answers section.

8 THE ROAD TO MANDALAY

1. *Eye, ear, arm, leg, toe, lip, hip, rib, jaw, gum, gut.* There are others.
2. *Slow up* and *slow down.*
3. *Sleuth.*
4. *Vacuum.*
5. *Unusual.*
6. *Are, area.*
7. *Polish.*

It was almost sunrise when I realized we were only about 20 km from my father's farm. "I'm going to turn your voice off," I said, "so you won't interrupt while I belt out 'The Road to Mandalay' in my deep, rich baritone. Do you like Kipling?"

"How should I know?" said the car. "I've never kippled."

Click.

My ballad was well timed. When I finished the last chorus, the dawn came up like thunder out of Tennessee across the Mississippi.

9 THE BLACK HOLE OF CAL CUTTER

Here is the paragraph:

> Perkins screamed and flung himself upon the floor;
> Margaret clutched at her heart with both hands; Dorothy,
> though her eyes looked like black holes in her white face,
> looked at him [DuQuesne] steadily and asked, "This is the
> end, then?"

Two readers, William Sears and James Fry, each calculated the sum
of the volumes of that endless sequence of cubes. It is $2.61237534\ldots$, an
irrational number surprisingly close to $(\sqrt{6}/4) + 2 = 2.61237243\ldots$. It is
sheer coincidence. Computer scientist R. William Gosper, Jr., checked
both numbers, and using what is called "integer linear programming" he
found an even more surprising coincidence: 81 divided by the cube of pi is
$2.612374289\ldots$.

A simpler infinite set of boxes with finite volume but infinite area and
length was proposed by Mike Steuben. Each box has a 1×1 base. The
first box is a cube of height 1. The second box has a height of $1/2$, the
third a height of $1/4$, and so on, with the denominators in a doubling
series. The total volume clearly is 2 cubic units, but both the length and
the total area of the tops is the sum of an infinite sequence of 1's.

10 SCIENCE FANTASY QUIZ

The following letter, with my rejoinder, appeared in the April 1985
issue of *Isaac Asimov's Science Fiction Magazine*:

Dear Martin Gardner,

> In the November 1984 issue you lay to rest the fallacy
> about the Great Wall of China being visible from the Moon.
> (Though the way I heard it, it was that the Great Wall was
> visible from space, presumably low Earth orbit. Is that true?
> If so, it would explain the error in the New York *Times*. ...

Martin Gardner comments:

> The New York *Times* (March 8, 1983) reported in its
> Topics column that the Great Wall is "the only mortal
> creation visible from the Moon." On March 20 the *Times*
> published a letter from a reader who said this was as absurd
> as seeing a popsicle stick from 384 kilometers. In the Topics
> column of the same issue, the *Times* apologized for its error.

11 THE BARBERS OF BARBERPOLIA

If you think about it long enough you should be able to see that if barber Y does a certain amount of work in y minutes, and barber Z does the same amount of work in z minutes, then the formula for x, the time it takes the two barbers to do the job together, is:

$$\frac{1}{x} = \frac{1}{y} + \frac{1}{z}$$

Applying the formula to our problem gives an answer of $6\frac{2}{3}$ minutes. Many people, without much thought, guess 15 minutes!

The formula has endless applications. Here are four:

1. If one man can mow a lawn in y units of time, and another can mow it in z units of time, the formula gives the time x it will take when both mow the lawn together.

2. If one faucet will fill a tank in y units of time, and another faucet will fill the same tank in z units of time, then x is the time it will take to fill the tank when both faucets are running.

3. If y is the distance of an object from a spherical lens, and z is the distance of the image from the lens, then x is the lens's focal length.

4. If two electrical resistors are in parallel, with resistances y and z, the total resistance is x.

Engineers and physicists know of many other examples of how this ridiculously simple formula applies to various aspects of the physical world.

12 IT'S ALL DONE WITH MIRRORS

Words consisting entirely of letters that are symmetrical with respect to a horizontal axis passing through their middles will not be altered when turned upside down and held up to a mirror. Only letters that are not the same above and below the axis will be changed. If you examine all the letters in the false statement, and imagine a horizontal line passing through the middle of the words, you will see that each letter has this kind of symmetry.

Letters with left-right symmetry (rather than top-bottom symmetry) are unchanged by a mirror if you hold them in front of the glass without turning them upside down. For example, if you print the word *automata* like this:

A
U
T
O
M
A
T
A

and hold it up to a mirror without inverting it, it will be unchanged in the glass.

If the topic of symmetry and its relation to the alphabet intrigues you, let me recommend Scott Kim's beautiful book *Inversions*. It is available in paperback, published in 1981 by Byte Books. Kim's clever calligraphy is as astonishing as good magic. The figure below shows two ways that Kim has lettered "Merry Christmas." The first has left-right symmetry and is unchanged when held in front of a mirror. The second has top-down symmetry, which you can prove by turning the page upside down and looking at its mirror reflection.

Now for a final question that I will leave unanswered so you and your friends can have the pleasure of debating it. Why does an ordinary mirror reverse only the left and right sides of things, never the tops and bottoms? It is hard to believe, but serious papers discussing this trivial question have actually been published in journals of philosophy! You'll find the references, and a thorough discussion of the problem, in Chapter 3 of my *The Ambidextrous Universe*.

13 SATAN AND THE APPLE

Recalling the two-line limerick, your mind completes the second one with:

> Whose limericks stopped on line one.

Unfortunately, if you finish the verse this way, you give it *two* lines, thereby injecting a whopping contradiction.

Now for a final paradox. There is a certain event that I guarantee will or will not take place during the next ten minutes. You are absolutely incapable of predicting correctly whether it will or won't occur. I don't mean that it's *unlikely* you can predict it. I mean it is *logically impossible* to predict it!

You don't believe it? Then do the following. If you think the event will occur, write "Yes" inside the blank rectangle below. If you think it won't happen, write "No" inside the rectangle.

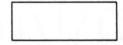

Now turn to the next answer section to find out what the event is, and how good your prediction was. If you predicted correctly, I'll send you a million dollars.

14 HOW'S-THAT-AGAIN FLANAGAN

A CONE

15 RELATIVISTICALLY SPEAKING

The doubling series—it consists of the consecutive powers of 2, starting with $2^0 = 1$—increases at what mathematicians call an exponential rate, reaching enormous numbers much sooner than seems possible. Between the 49th and the 50th cigarette the elapsed time would be $2^{48} = 281,474,976,710,656$ seconds. There are 60 seconds to a minute, 60 minutes to an hour, 24 hours to a day, and 365 days to a year. (We ignore leap years to simplify the calculation.) To convert the time in seconds to time in years we must divide by $60 \times 60 \times 24 \times 365 = 31,536,000$. The result is more than 8,925,512 years!

Actually, Pulver would probably kick the habit after his 25th cigarette because he would have to wait more than six months before he smoked the next one. Suppose you wanted to determine the total of all waiting times up to a certain power of 2. Would you have to add all the powers to get the sum? No, there is a marvelous short cut. [See the Third Answers section.]

17

16 BAR BETS ON THE BAGEL

"I'm wrong," said Pulver. "Make that next drink a double Marstini."

17 CATCH THE BEM

The towns on the map fall into two parity sets: those with four roads joined to them, and those with three. The figure below shows all the even towns circled. Observe that every path from an even town leads to an odd town, and vice versa. Therefore any path on the network must alternate odd and even towns.

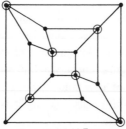

Even and Odd Towns

Along a path the number of even towns is equal to the number of odd towns (when two end towns are of *opposite* parity), or there is an additional town of one set (when the two end towns have the *same* parity).

Count the number of towns of each parity. Eight are odd, and six are even. The difference is more than one. It is not possible, therefore, for a path to visit each town just once. There will always be at least one town not on the path.

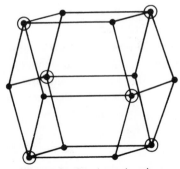

Rhombic Dodecahedron

As this figure shows, the network is combinatorially the same as the skeleton of a simple convex polyhedron called a rhombic dodecahedron, a form often taken by crystals of garnet. H. S. M. Coxeter, a famous University of Toronto geometer, was the first to find the above proof that the skeleton has no Hamiltonian path. It is the simplest known polyhedron of this type. As far as I know, no one has yet proved that every polyhedron with fewer than 14 vertices has a skeleton with a Hamiltonian path.

18 ANIMAL TTT

If you checkerboard color each animal as shown on the facing page you'll see that each has two black and two white cells except for Knobby, who has three cells of one color and one of the other. Therefore the five pieces cannot tile any figure unless, when it is checkerboard colored, it has an excess of two cells of one color. The 4 × 5 rectangle has an equal number of black and white cells, making it impossible to tile unless you slice Knobby into two parts.

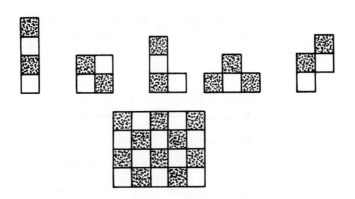

19 PLAYING SAFE ON THE BAGEL

The safe spot is NOWHERE (no W here).

Now for an entertaining problem that won't be answered because that would spoil the fun. Imagine a chess king placed on one of the letters. By moving one cell at a time in any direction—up, down, left, right, and diagonally—you can spell various words. For example, you can spell such names as LEM, TUTU, and POPOV, and words such as GNU, ELM, VOW, NUTS, MELTS, STUNTS, STUNG, and BAHAI.

Your task is to spell an adjective that describes the state of Ensign Pulver after he has imbibed too many Martian martinis.

20 SEX AMONG THE POLYOMANS

Solutions to the four problems are shown below. Only the upper right and lower left solutions are unique. These patterns, generously supplied by Dr. Matsu, are only warm-ups for two more difficult tasks.

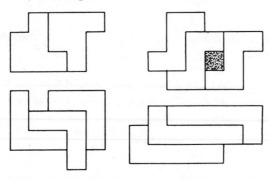

Divide the T-shaped animal into four identical 5-cell creatures.

Divide the shape on the right into two identical 9-cell animals. For many people this is a tough problem. [See the next answer section.]

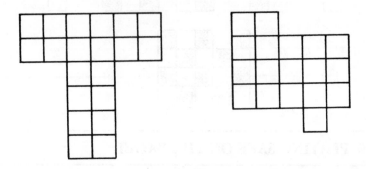

Dissection problems of this sort—cutting a figure into two or more congruent parts—abound in the puzzle books of Sam Loyd and Henry Ernest Dudeney. See also my column on the topic in *Scientific American*, July 1977.

21 INNER PLANETS QUIZ

5. Mercury has a weak magnetic field. It's not as strong as the Earth's, but it is stronger than the magnetic fields of Venus and Mars. No one knows why Mercury has such a field, but then no one really knows for sure why the Earth has one.

6a. The angular velocity of the Earth's orbital motion around the Sun is

$$\frac{1}{365.24}\frac{\text{revolutions}}{\text{day}}, \quad \text{that of Venus is} \quad \frac{1}{224.7}\frac{\text{revolutions}}{\text{day}}.$$

The angle subtended by the two planets viewed from the Sun, see Figure, increases at the rate given by the difference of these two rates, which is

$$.00171245\frac{\text{revolutions}}{\text{day}}.$$

It takes 584.0 days for this angle to increase by one complete revolution.

6b. During this time, the line segment ES from the Earth to the Sun makes

$$\frac{584}{365.24} = 1.5990$$

revolutions from west to east, so the new position of EV is 1.5990 revolutions to the east of the old, and this is the net amount by which the line segment EV from Earth to Venus has turned with respect to the fixed stars during this time, as we now explain.

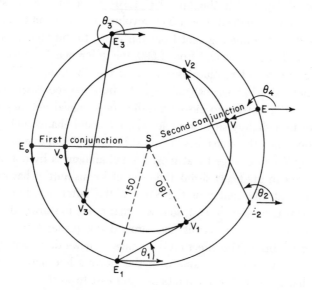

If Venus stayed on the line segment from the sun to the Earth all the time, it would be quite clear that EV made 1.5990 revolutions. However, Venus orbits the sun at a faster rate, and EV turns at a variable rate. For short periods it even turns from east to west. However, since the orbit of Venus is entirely inside the orbit of Earth, the net amount by which EV turns during 584 days (i.e. the total amount of west to east minus the total east to west) will be the same as if Venus had in fact stayed on the Sun-Earth line segment all the time. This is, we hope, fairly clear; we refer those who want a hint of a rigorous proof to the end of this discussion.

The amount by which Venus actually turns around its axis in the 584.0 days between conjunctions is $584/243 = 2.403$ revolutions from east to west. This has to be added to the apparent rotation of 1.599 revolutions we computed. So, viewed from earth, Venus seems to have undergone $2.403 + 1.599 = 3.998$ revolutions from east to west. If this were exactly 4 it would mean the same hemisphere of Venus would be turned toward Earth at each conjunction, and some astronomers believe this will indeed turn out to be the case when additional observations become available. That would be too extraordinary a coincidence to be an accident, but it is equally mysterious how the feeble gravity of the Earth could have noticeably affected the rotation of Venus. (A mosquito could support a boxing champion on its back at that distance if the Earth's pull were all it had to contend with.)

Finally, we give the promised more rigorous argument that the net amount T by which the line EV turns from east to west between conjunctions is indeed the 1.599 revolutions we would get if Venus remained on the line segment from the Earth to the Sun throughout the motion. If T were different from 1.599, the difference D would have to be a whole number of revolutions, otherwise the direction of EV at the end could not be what we calculated it to be. Now consider what would happen if Venus were to move with the same angular velocity around the sun, but in a slightly smaller circle. Then T could change only slightly, at most. But since these changes, D, must be multiples of one revolution, the only way T can change by at most a small amount is by not changing at all. So we can gradually shrink the orbit of Venus until it has radius 0, i.e. until it is at the center of the Sun. In the latter situation T is 1.599 revolutions from west to east, so it was that much to start with. So the line along which we view Venus goes around the planet from west to east 1.599 revolutions. The effect on the image is, if we disregard the effect of changes in distance, the same as if the viewing line had been fixed and Venus had rotated 1.599 revolutions from east to west.

7. The moon's pull on the Earth is slightly stronger on the side of Earth facing it than on the opposite side. As a result, the moon simultaneously pulls up the ocean water on the side nearest it, and pulls the Earth slightly away from the water on the opposite side. This produces high tides on both sides of the Earth.

8. The lady could be a native of Mars, Pennsylvania. There is a Mercury and Earth in Texas, and towns called Venus are in Texas, Florida, Nebraska, and Pennsylvania.

22 PUZZLES IN FLATLAND

Turn the board and its counters (or the page) upside down.

William Higginson, in his article "Mathematizing 'Frogs'" (*Mathematics Teacher*, October 1981), discussed the classic counter-moving puzzle. At the end of his article he proposed analyzing the 8-cell board shown here but did not specify any particular tasks.

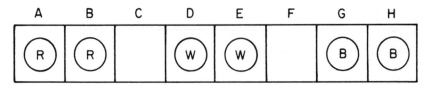

In *Mathematical Digest* (July 1985), published by the University of Capetown, I reproduced this board and proposed the following rules for two problems. The counters are red, white and blue as indicated. Any counter may move once in either direction to an adjacent empty space, or it may jump once in any direction over a counter of any color to an empty space immediately beyond. What are the minimum number of moves needed to:

1. Permute the colors cyclically. That is, change the order of pairs to white, blue, red, ending with the same pattern (except for the colors) as at the start. I conjectured that the best solution is first to exchange red and white (8 moves), then exchange red (now in the center) and blue (8 moves). Total moves: 16.

2. Exchange the two end colors. I could not do this in less than 22 moves.

Michael James, an 18-year-old student in Durhan, South Africa, improved both solutions. He solved the first problem in 15 moves, the second in 20. (See next answer section.)

A proof of the $n(n + 2)$ formula for the standard puzzle (one empty cell between n black and n white counters) is in Higginson's article, and in Benjamin L. Schwartz's solution to Problem 952, *Mathematics Magazine* (November 1976).

23 DIRAC'S SCISSORS

"That's not a question, but a statement," said Dirac. "Next question, please."

24 BULL'S-EYES AND PRATFALLS

All the remarks were made by Thomas Edison. I found the first three in *The Experts Speak* (cited earlier), and the fourth in a section on predictions in *A Random Walk in Science*, compiled by R. L. Weber (1973).

25 FLARP FLIPS ANOTHER FIVER

As Tanya explained, you toss the coin twice. If *HH*, person *A* pays. If *HT*, person *B* pays, and if *TH*, person *C* pays. If the coin falls tails twice, you make another pair of tosses.

The decision can come with two tosses. There is no required maximum, but the probability of a decision after *n* pairs of tosses approaches 1 so rapidly that one is practically certain to be reached quickly.

As readers know, Tanya enjoys word play as much as recreational math. She picked up Flarp's pen and jotted down the triplet of letters *SPB*. "Can you tell me what familiar English word has those three letters in it, side by side and in that order?"

Flarp and Pulver puzzled over the problem for about ten minutes without getting anywhere.

"Here's a hint," said Tanya. She pushed the pink tip of her tongue through her lips and blew such a loud Bronx cheer that all the people in the lounge swiveled their heads and looked startled.

You will find the word in the Third Answers section.

28 ALICE IN BEELAND

William Vanderlinde and Tom Knight each solved the problem of placing five non-attacking bee-rooks on the order-8 triangle in a simple way. I had mentioned that the maximum number of such pieces is five. By adding a bottom row of eight empty cells to the solution I gave for the order-7 triangle on p. 59, which also holds five rooks, they obtained a solution that differed from the one I gave in the First Answers section.

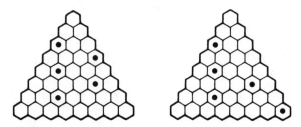

Paul D. Hobson sent a third solution, along with the other two. It is obtained from the pattern just described (see above, left) by moving the spot at the top right down to the lower right corner (see above, right).

Herbert Taylor supplied the solutions below for triangles of orders 9 through 13:

28

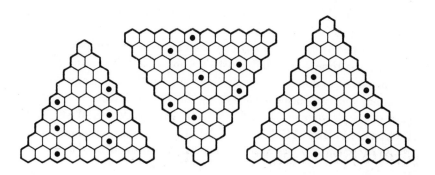

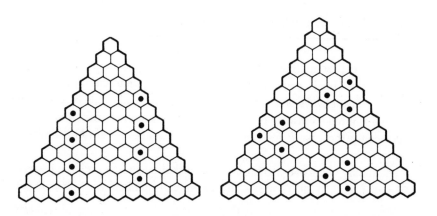

A solution with two beelines is shown below. I am indebted to Michael D. Hoffa for this solution.

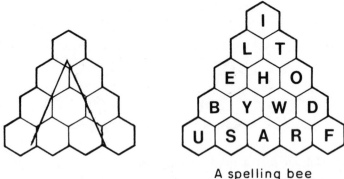

A spelling bee

As everybody knows, bees are expert spellers. It is not surprising that many of their puzzles involve spelling words and sentences on hexagonally-tesselated patterns. In the order 5 triangle you see a spelling-bee problem that Herb showed Alice before she wandered off to explore another region of Wonderland.

Your task is to start on any cell, then move like a bee-rook—but only *one* cell at a time—to spell the first six words of a well known poem. You are allowed to double a letter by "moving" to the cell you are on. For example, you can spell such words as HOOT and HELL. It's surprising how many words can be spelled on this pattern: WHY, WAR, THEY, DWARF, LITHE, BYE-BYE, WAYWARD, and dozens of others.

The poem, by the way, is one of the many poems that Carroll parodies in his *Alice* books. See the Third Answers section.

29 HUSTLE OFF TO BUFFALO

After experimenting with a few hundred sets of randomly chosen integers, the Hustle concluded that regardless of what the numbers are, the procedure always ends with a set of zeros. Actually, this is so even if we have k integers instead of four, provided k is a power of 2. Below, we discuss only the case $k = 4$, and we give references for further information.

You may want to try to prove yourself that when k is odd, the process will never lead to all 0's unless all the original numbers are equal. Don't look at the next solution section too soon to see why this is so, since you may be annoyed that you did not take the time to hit upon the reason for this yourself.

Returning to $k = 4$, we now prove that the process will terminate for integers; and we will sketch a proof of why it will also terminate for four randomly chosen real numbers. As you will see, the words "randomly chosen" are used advisedly here.

Let a, b, c, d be a quadruple of real numbers in the given cyclic order, i.e. d is next to a. The number of differencing operations one has to perform to get $0, 0, 0, 0$ will be called the *level* of a, b, c, d; if we never get four 0's we say the level is infinite. We first present two easy cases where the level is ≤ 6. At this stage we do not yet need to assume that a, b, c, d are integers. They can be arbitrary real numbers.

If one of our numbers is $\geq$ both of its neighbors, we call it locally maximal, or a local maximum. A locally minimal number is defined similarly. Either one is called a local extremum. Note that equality is allowed. For instance, if three of the numbers are equal, the middle one is both locally maximal and minimal.

Case (i): The quadruple a, b, c, d contains a local minimum and a local maximum which are not next to each other. Suppose b is a local minimum and d is a local maximum. Then the absolute differences are

$$a' = a - b, \quad b' = c - b, \quad c' = d - c, \quad d' = d - a.$$

The next set of differences is $|c - a|, |b - 2c + d|, |c - a|, |d - 2a + b|$. Since the first and third are identical, we denote this quadruple by

(1) $a'', b'', a'', c''.$

The third set of absolute differences has the form A, A, B, B. The fourth set has the form $0, A', 0, A'$. The fifth set is A', A', A', A', and the sixth set is $0, 0, 0, 0$.

Case (ii): There exist two nonadjacent local maxima or minima. One can prove in a manner similar to the above that the level is ≤ 6 in this case too; we leave this as an exercise.

We can combine the above two cases in the following statement: *if the quadruple a, b, c, d contains two nonadjacent local extrema, then its level is ≤ 6.*

We next note that *if two of the four numbers are equal then the level is also ≤ 6.* Indeed, if the equal numbers are nonadjacent, then the level is ≤ 4, as we deduced from (1) above. If they are adjacent then they are both local extrema, and at least one of the other two numbers must be maximal or minimal, so there are at least three local extrema, and two among these must be nonadjacent.

One may think the cases not yet covered could be disposed of in a similar way, but that is not so. As we shall see in the Third Answers section, there exist quadruples of arbitrarily high level as well as quadruples of infinitely high level.

Nevertheless, we can quickly show that a quadruple a, b, c, d of integers has finite level. We may assume without loss of generality that a, b, c, d are all positive. (Adding the same constant to all of them will accomplish that without changing the level, except in the trivial case when all the numbers are 0.) If we now form the absolute differences we do not get any 0's as long as the level is > 5, since that could happen only if two numbers at the previous level had been equal, and that can not occur at a level > 6. If all four numbers of a quadruple are positive, then the largest among the absolute differences is smaller than the largest among the original numbers. This means that if our starting numbers are positive integers, we must get down to a level 6 in no more steps than the largest of the original numbers. (In fact the number of steps needed is much smaller, as will be seen from the argument below.) Thus a quadruple of integers always has finite level. It follows immediately that *a quadruple of rational numbers also has finite level*.

Now try to find a quadruple of infinite level. Clearly its members cannot all be rational. Before looking at the Third Answers section, consider the following hint: We are concerned with differences, and we know that the differences of adjacent terms in a geometric progression form a geometric progression with the *same* common ratio!

---

31 PUZZLE FLAGS ON MARS

We first derive a very simple algebraic representation of 3×3 magic squares.

Let S be the common sum of every row, column and diagonal. Let a be the number in the middle of the square. Adding all three rows we find:

(1)   The sum of all 9 elements of the square $= 3S$.

If we add the entries in the two diagonals and the middle row and the middle column, we find that

(2) $4a + (\text{the sum of all elements except } a) = 4S.$

Subtract equation (1) from equation (2):

$$3a = S \quad \text{or} \quad a = \frac{1}{3}S.$$

Let the entry in the upper right hand corner of the magic square be $a + b$ and the entry in the upper left hand corner, $a + c$. (The numbers b and c thus defined can be negative.) Since the sum in each diagonal is $3a$, the entries in the lower left and lower right corners are $a - b$ and $a - c$. We now have represented the elements in the four corners and, of course, in the center; the missing entries can be found from the condition that each of the outside rows and columns has the sum $3a$.

We represent the result in the following way:

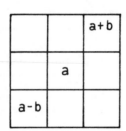

The numbers which occur in our magic square are the nine numbers of the form

(3) $a + ib + jc \quad (i, j = -1, 0, 1).$

Each of the three parts of our diagram shows a triplet corresponding to a fixed value of j; each triplet forms an arithmetic progression. We can say: The nine numbers in 3×3 magic square can be arranged into 3 triplets in such a way that the numbers in each triplet are in arithmetic progression with the same common difference. Moreover, the lowest terms of the triplets are also in arithmetic progression.

Conversely, if one has nine numbers satisfying the above conditions, they can be written in the form (3); we can take the difference within each triplet as b, the difference between the lowest members of the triplets as c and the middle number of the middle triplet as a.

If the nine numbers are to be consecutive positive integers, then $a = 5$, and either $b = \pm 1$ and $c = \pm 3$, or $b = \pm 3$ and $c = \pm 1$.

Observe that on the *lo shu* 8 is in a corner. Move the 8 to a side cell as shown below.

Can you place eight other whole numbers (non-negative integers) in the eight blank cells to form a magic square (no two numbers alike) with each row, each column, and each of the two main diagonals adding to 15 —the same as the magic constant of the *lo shu*?

32 THE VANISHING PLANK

Here is how the Great Aleph proved that the plank, although horrendously mutilated, had not disappeared. He simply placed on top of it a piece of plank slightly longer than 1/4 of the original. Keeping it horizontal, he slid it back and forth across the invisible plank, from one end to the other. It did not fall through because every gap left by the infinite operation of slicing was shorter than 1/4.

The Great Aleph concluded the illusion by pressing his palms against the ends of the invisible plank, then moving them inward. This pushed all the points together, forming in midair a plank half the size of the original. To prove it solid, the Great Aleph snapped it in half with a quick karate chop, after which he bowed to thunderous applause from all the creatures in the audience who had hands.

The fantastic plank trick derives from a famous infinite set first described by Cantor, and known as the "Cantor discontinuum." In Cantor's version, at each step the segments of a line of length 1 are trisected and the central third removed. It is easy to show that at the limit the sum of the removed sections is 1, yet an infinite set of points remains. Although there are as many points in this remnant as there were in the original segment, between every two of these points there is a gap.

You'll find a good discussion of Cantor's mind-boggling discontinuum in *What is Mathematics?*, a classic work by Richard Courant and Herbert Robbins. I based my description of the Great Aleph's illusion on "Cantor's Disappearing Table," an article by Larry E. Knop that appeared in *The College Mathematics Journal*, November 1985.

33   987654321

4. If the number of digits not counting the last one in $N = 100\ldots01$ is one less than a number which has an odd factor > 1, then N can be factored. We again show how this works on a typical example. Suppose we have 17 0's. We are going to use the odd factor 3 (of 18). We represent N as a sum of 3 terms with alternating signs as follows:

$$
\begin{array}{rr}
 & 100000100000000000000 \\
- & 1000001000000 \\
+ & 1000001 \\
\hline
N = & 100000000000000000001.
\end{array}
$$

Since all three summands are multiples of 1000001, this is a factor of N.

The factoring we gave is valid no matter what the base is, as is the factoring theorem for numbers in which all the digits are equal. Both are disguised forms of identities you probably encountered in algebra.

Readers were asked to find a rearrangement of the numbers on a clock so that no triplet of adjacent numbers has a sum higher than 21. One answer: $1, 8, 10, 3, 5, 9, 4, 6, 11, 2, 7, 12$.

I found this problem in Dean S. Clark's paper, "A Combinatorial Theorem on Circulant Matrices," in *American Mathematical Monthly* (December 1985). Clark gives a short proof that the highest sum such a triplet can have, in any circular permutation of numbers 1 through 12, can't be less than 21, but he does not know how many permutations achieve this lowest bound.

The answer (not counting mirror reflections as different) is 261. If mirror reflections are counted, it is 522. Tim Rolfe, Tom Broce, David Smith, and Fred Galvin were the first to send me the results of their computer program for the problem.

35 THE WISDOM OF SOLOMON

Solomon put one gold talent in bowl A, and the other 19 in bowl B.

The figure below shows how a simple inverted-tree graph gives the probability that Solomon will choose a gold talent. The probability of selecting either bowl is 1/2.

If bowl A is chosen, the probability of taking a gold talent from it is 1, or certain. We multiply this by 1/2 to get a probability of 1/2 that Solomon will take the single gold talent in bowl A.

In general, on such a graph, the probability of the event at each end-point of the upside-down tree is obtained by multiplying the probabilities that mark the branches leading from the end-point to the tree's "root" at the top.

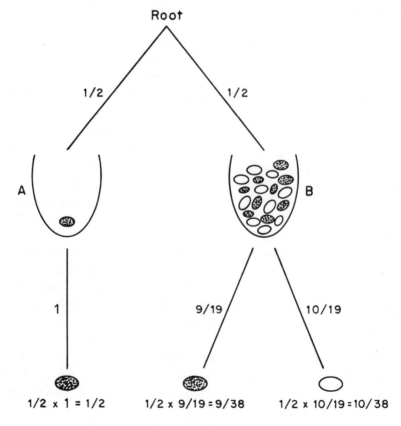

Tree Graph for Solomon's Problem

If bowl B is chosen, the probability of taking a gold talent from it is 9/19. We multiply this by 1/2 to get a probability of 9/38 that Solomon will take a gold talent from bowl B.

The two probabilities are now added. The sum of 1/2 and 9/38 is 14/19 = .736 + or almost 3/4. This is the probability that Solomon will draw a gold talent if he selects a bowl at random, then takes from it a talent.

Did Solomon and Sheba actually wed? Eastern lore has it that Sheba, although beautiful, had extremely hairy legs, and Solomon refused to marry her until she had the hair removed by a jinni. The Ethiopians believe that Sheba bore Solomon a son who became that nation's first king. All later kings of Ethiopia traced their lineage back to Solomon and the Queen of Sheba. The Old Testament's 45th Psalm has been interpreted by some commentators as a prophecy of those events.

Moslem fundamentalists believe that Allah gave Solomon power to control the jinni, the Koran's counterparts of Old Testament demons. Through this power Solomon was said to acquire numerous magic devices. A carpet of green silk carried him wherever he wished, with a flock of birds always flying overhead like a canopy to shield him from the sun. Both Jewish and Islamic folklore speak of an enchanted signet-ring that would whisper the answer to any question.

Solomon's greatest weakness, says the Bible (I Kings 11:1-3), was that he "loved many strange women ... and he had seven hundred wives ... and three hundred concubines." These ladies—including Solomon's first wife, daughter of the great Pharaoh of Egypt—were constantly quarreling. To end this bickering, Solomon invented an intriguing checker-like board game that he taught the ladies. Costly prizes were given to the winners of round-robin tournaments and problem contests. Known as "Solomon," the game is now on sale in the United States. If you're curious, you can get details by writing to Kadon Enterprises, 1227 Lorene Drive, Pasadena, MD 21122. The company makes and sells a variety of handsome mathematical games and puzzles.

The board on which Solomon is played is the familiar Star of David (sometimes called a hexagram) with three added lines that join opposite corners (see figure on next page). It is a graph that lends itself to dozens of fascinating puzzles. Here are a few:

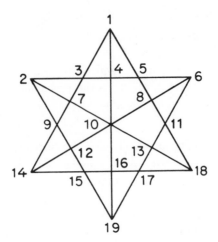

35

1. Can 19 trees be planted to form nine straight rows with five trees in each row? The graph provides a solution.

2. Can numbers 1 through 19 be placed on the graph's spots to make a magic star, each row of five adding to the same number?

3. How many different triangles can be traced in the pattern? How many different quadrilaterals?

4. If the star's corners are joined by lines to make a complete graph for those six points (all other points are taken as intersections where lines go under or over one another), can the 15 lines be made to go under and over in such manner that it is impossible to trace a closed curve that is knotted?

5. Using rules formulated by Leonhard Euler, it is easy to show that the Solomon graph cannot be traversed by one continuous path that does not go over any line segment twice. Such a path is possible if and only if all the points are the meeting points of an even number of lines, or if there are just two "odd" points. In the second case, the path clearly must begin and end on the two odd points. The graph has six odd points, therefore three separate paths are required for traversing it.

Suppose, however, you are allowed to traverse a line segment twice, and/or walk outside the graph. What is the shortest continuous path that goes over all the line segments?

6. Trace the graph on cardboard, then cut along the lines to make 18 pieces. It is easy to fit them together, without gaps or overlaps, to make rectangles and rhombi of various shapes. Can you make an equilateral triangle? Can you prove that the 18 pieces will not form a square or regular hexagon?

7. Solomon Solitaire is played as follows. Put a counter on every spot except one. Any counter may jump any adjacent counter (as in checkers) if the next point is vacant. The jumped counter is removed. Can you remove all counters except one which will end on the only spot that initially had no counter?

In view of the graph's six-fold symmetry, there are only four essentially different spots for the hole. All are solvable with the final counter on the hole spot. If a chain of jumps is counted as a single move, as in checkers, the minimum number of moves required for each hole is not yet known. I will give a 9-move solution for the hole in the center.

A marvelous book about peg solitaire, and the combinatorial theory behind it, is *The Ins and Outs of Peg Solitaire*, by John D. Beasley (Oxford University Press, 1985).

36 THANG, THE PLANET EATER

The needed insight is that half of any odd number added to one-half is an integer. It is never necessary, therefore, for Thang to eat just half a planet. If you started by assuming he did that, you probably got hopelessly lost.

We are told that at the end of the seventh day all the planets had been eaten. This could happen only if Thang ate a single planet on the last day (one-half plus one-half makes one). We now work backward by doubling and adding one. On the sixth day there would be $2 + 1 = 3$ planets. Doubling and adding 1 at each step generates the sequence $1, 3, 7, 15, 31, 63, 127$. There were 127 planets at the start. Thang ate them all in a descending sequence of the powers of two: $64, 32, 16, 8, 4, 2, 1$.

Observe that the numbers in the sequence of planets available for eating each day $(1, 3, 7, \ldots)$ are each one less than a power of 2. Numbers of this type, expressed by the formula $2^n - 1$, are called Mersenne numbers. We encountered such numbers on pages 109–111 in connection with perfect numbers. If the number is also a prime (divisible only by itself and 1) it is called a Mersenne prime. The total number of planets eaten by Thang, 127, is the fourth Mersenne prime. Only 30 such primes were known in 1986, and no mathematician knows whether their number is infinite or finite. The largest known prime, $2^{216091} - 1$, is a Mersenne prime. It was discovered in 1985 by a Cray supercomputer owned by Chevron Geosciences, in Houston, using a program written by David

Slowinski, of Cray Research, in Chippewa Falls, Wisconsin. The new Mersenne prime has 65,050 digits.

Now try your skill on one more problem. Finding still another solar system, Thang threw away one planet (he didn't like the way it smelled), then ate 1/11 of those that remained. On the second day he threw away two planets and ate 1/11 of those that were left. On the third day he tossed away three planets, and so on, each time eating 1/11 of what remained. In other words, on each nth day he threw away n planets before eating 1/11 of the rest. Eventually, all the planets were gone.

How many planets were there in the solar system, and how many days did it take to eliminate them? The answer is in the Third Answers section.

THIRD ANSWERS

1 RIDDLES OF THE SPHINX

The chart below shows how a sphinx population, starting with one L-sphinx on day zero, grows during the first week. Our question is answered in the bottom line: On the afternoon of the seventh day there are 16,384 sphinxes, of which 8,128 are left forms, and 8,256 are right. Observe that the total number of sphinxes always equals 4^n, and the difference between left and right forms always equals $\pm 2^n$.

n (days)	L-sphinxes	R-sphinxes	Total	Difference $|L - R|$
0	1	0	1	1
1	1	3	4	2
2	10	6	16	4
3	28	36	64	8
4	136	120	256	16
5	496	528	1024	32
6	2080	2016	4096	64
7	8128	8256	16384	128

Now for a more difficult problem. Can you devise formulas that will give the number of left and right forms when you are given n, the number of elapsed days? The answer in the Fourth Answers section will introduce you to an important distinction between what mathematicians call recursive and nonrecursive formulas.

2 PRECOGNITION AND THE MYSTIC SEVEN

To discover why all 2-digit sequences except $00, 33, 66, 99$ occur exactly once in the 96 digit period of $1/97$, we look at the Remainder R at some stage of the division process. In usual long division, when we "bring down" the next 0, we compute the integer part of $10R/97$ to find the next digit. We can find the next pair of digits (either of which may be 0) by computing the integer part $[100R/97]$ of $100R/97$.

We now use that $100/97$ is just a little bit greater than 1 to evaluate the integer part of $100R/97$ for all 96 values of R:

$$\left[\frac{100}{97}R\right] = R + \left[\frac{3}{97}R\right] = \begin{cases} R \text{ for } 1 \leq R \leq 32 \\ R + 1 \text{ for } 33 \leq R \leq 64 \\ R + 2 \text{ for } 65 \leq R \leq 96. \end{cases}$$

We see that all positive integers up to 98 occur in our sequence except 33 and 66 which are jumped over.

Circular sequences of digits whose segments of length n are all different and every possible one occurs exactly once were first considered and applied by the French engineer J.M.E. Baudot (1845–1903) for whom the baud was named. [The baud is a unit for measuring the speed of information transfer; 1 baud = 1 bit/sec.] The period of $1/97$ could be made into a Baudot sequence by inserting next to one occurrence of each of 0, 3, 6 and 9 a second digit of the same kind.

Long division of numbers does not yield many Baudot sequences but one can construct them very easily by long division of polynomials whose coefficients are elements of finite fields. See the book *Shift Register Sequences*, by S.W. Golomb of polyomino fame.

Your rear end is on the paper, and you got your shoes on your feet.

3 ON TO CHARMIAN

The word is CHAIRMAN. Richard Guy asks: Is the chairman poor or wealthy? Answer with a three-word anagram! [See next answer section.]

4 TECHNOLOGY IN VZIGS

The following letter, and my reply, appeared in the November 1984 issues of *Isaac Asimov's Science Fiction Magazine*:

> Dear Martin Gardner,
>   Another way to waste my time! Enclosed is a list of extremely uninteresting, mostly exotic words, which fit the criteria of your "Technology on VZIGS" article.
>   About halfway through my word search I found this one—something straight out of the Twilight Zone. The word "wizard," recoded, becomes "draziw"—its reverse. It is enough to make one wonder if there might be something in nomenology or numerology or whatever. Then again, maybe not.
>   Even for someone whose life includes exquisitely dull periods this project provided a new low. "EFTS"—"VUGH." Ugh, indeed! Please do not ask me to do this sort of thing again. I've always had a warm regard for you and hate to refuse you anything, but enough is enough.
>
> Yours truly,
Patricia W. Moore,
Golden Valley, MN.

Mrs. Moore was the first to respond to my request for English words that become other words in a reverse alphabet cipher. Among the four and five-letter word pairs she discovered are: *girl-trio, girth-trigs, grogs-tilth*. So far, no six-letter examples are known. The fact that *wizard* turns into *wizard* backwards is truly astonishing.

Other respondents included Theodore Beck, of Stanton, CA, who sent a list of 53 word pairs. Carl Kadie, of Urbana, IL, concocted this sentence: *Oft Levi Mix told Zig, lug over NRC glow art*. The cipher text reads: *Lug over NRC glow art, often Levi Mix told Zig*. Incidentally, Leopold Bloom, in James Joyce's *Ulysses*, uses a reverse alphabet cipher to record the name and address of a woman with whom he is having a clandestine correspondence.

6 AROUND THE SOLAR SYSTEM

If the dime has a diameter smaller than the side of a cell, it is easy to see that it can pass over a portion of each cell in two moves. If the dime's diameter is larger than a cell's side, *one* move is sufficient, as shown below:

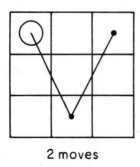   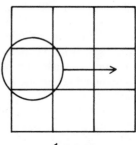

           2 moves   1 move

The original problem obviously generalizes to lattice cells in any rectangular array, as well as to cells in triangular arrays and other patterns. Many such tasks, often in the form of chess queen "tours," can be found in the puzzle books of Sam Loyd and Henry E. Dudeney. A pioneering paper on the general problem is "Unicursal Polygonal Paths and other graphs on lattice points," by Solomon W. Golomb and John L. Selfridge, in the *Pi Mu Epsilon Journal*, Vol. 6 (Fall 1970), pages 101–117. Here the task is to find polygonal paths through lattice points rather than cells.

To whet your interest in this still largely unexplored area of recreational graph theory, consider the 3 × 4 and 4 × 4 arrays shown below:

The dots are to be traversed by a continuous path of straight line segments. A closed or "reentrant" path is one that ends where it began, not necessarily on a lattice point. Otherwise, the path is open. The points of each of these lattices can be traversed with as few as six line segments, but closed paths are much harder to obtain than open ones. See if you can find a closed 6-line tour for each pattern.

7 THE STRIPE OF BARBERPOLIA

The height will be the same as the distance between parallel sides. More generally, if the base is a polygon circumscribed about a circle, the prism with minimal area will have height equal to the diameter of the circle.

13 SATAN AND THE APPLE

The event is: You will write "No" inside the rectangle.

I introduced this version of a well known prediction paradox in Chapter 11 of *New Mathematical Diversions from Scientific American* (1966). It is one of the simplest of many prediction paradoxes that can arise whenever a prediction is causally related to the event being predicted. It can be further simplified by asking someone to reply yes or no to your question: "Will your reply be no?"

For a discussion of two famous prediction paradoxes, much harder to analyze than the one given here, see "The Paradox of the Unexpected Hanging," in my *Unexpected Hanging and Other Mathematical Diversions* (Simon and Schuster, 1969), and the two chapters on Newcomb's Paradox in my *Knotted Doughnuts and Other Mathematical Entertainments* (W.H. Freeman, 1986).

15

15 RELATIVISTICALLY SPEAKING

The sum of the first n powers of 2, starting with $2^0 = 1$, is $2^{n+1} - 1$. For example, the sum of the first ten powers of 2 is $2^{11} - 1 = 2,047$. Here is a simple proof by mathematical induction:

The formula is certainly true for $n = 1$. If

$$1 + 2 + 2^2 + \cdots + 2^{n-1} = 2^n - 1,$$

then, adding 2^n to both sides, we get

$$1 + 2 + 2^2 + \cdots + 2^{n-1} + 2^n = 2^n - 1 + 2^n = 2^{n+1} - 1.$$

20 SEX AMONG THE POLYOMANS

Here are the unique solutions to the two dissection problems:

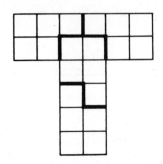 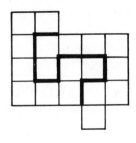

22 PUZZLES IN FLATLAND

The 15-move cyclic permutation (R = right, L = left):

DL,	BR,	DR,	AR,	BR
CL,	EL,	CL,	GL,	HL
FR,	DR,	EL,	GL,	FR

The 20-move exchange of red and blue:

ER,	BR,	DL,	GL,	EL
CR,	ER,	AR,	CR,	DL
FL,	HL,	GR,	ER,	CL
DR,	FL,	DL,	BR,	CL.

25 FLARP FLIPS ANOTHER FIVER

The word is RASPBERRY.

It's a choice example of a word once available to poets, but now damaged by its acquired meaning. The Oxford English Dictionary's *Supplement* traces this uncouth use of the word back to 1915, but fails to explain its origin. Here's a lovely quatrain from "Daisy," by Francis Thompson, that is impossible to read today without chuckling:

Her beauty smoothed earth's furrowed face!
She gave me tokens three:
A look, a word of her winsome mouth,
And a wild raspberry.

Two science-fiction writers sent explanations of how "raspberry" came to mean what in the United States is called a "Bronx cheer"—a term said to have originated in the National Theater, in the Bronx, New York. See the next answer section.

28 ALICE IN BEELAND

The solution to the spelling-bee puzzle is the opening line of Isaac Watts's poem "Against Idleness and Mischief." The first stanza is:

How doth the little busy bee
    Improve each shining hour,
And gather honey all the day
    From every opening flower.

Lewis Carroll's parody begins:

How doth the little crocodile
    Improve his shining tail,
And pour the waters of the Nile
    On every golden scale.

29 HUSTLE OFF TO BUFFALO

Suppose k is odd, and the numbers are $a_1, \ldots, a_k$. We show that if these numbers are not all equal then the absolute values of the differences $a_i' = a_{i+1} - a_i$ ($i = 1, \ldots, k$; $a_{k+1} = a_1$) are not all equal either. The reason is that the sum of all these differences is 0. If the absolute values were all the same, the sum could be 0 only if positive and negative signs were to occur in equal numbers among them, which can not happen if k is odd. Thus taking absolute differences can not produce equal numbers if the original numbers were not all equal, and we never get all 0's.

Our observation at the end of the second answer suggests that a quadruple of the form

$$(1) \qquad a = 1, \quad b = x, \quad c = x^2, \quad d = x^3$$

may give absolute differences which are just multiples of the original numbers. We find that if $x > 1$, the absolute differences a', b', c' are $x - 1$ times a, b, c, while $d' = x^3 - 1 = (x - 1)(x^2 + x + 1)$. Thus if

$$(2) \qquad x^3 = x^2 + x + 1,$$

then forming the differences just multiplies the numbers by $x - 1$ and we never get 0's. Equation (2) has one real solution which is, of course, irrational, and approximately 1.839286755. So the approximate value of this quadruple of infinite level is

$$(3) \qquad 1, 1.839286755, 3.382975769, 6.222262522,$$

and rational quadruples which are close to this will have a high level.

Multiplying the above quadruple by a nonzero constant and adding another constant to each element will of course produce other quadruples of infinite level; but, surprisingly, *these are the only quadruples of infinite level that exist*. To see this we need some more inequalities, and we shall also need matrix theory. See the Fourth Answers section.

31

31 PUZZLE FLAGS ON MARS

1	8	6
10	5	0
4	2	9

Did you forget that zero is a non-negative integer?

Here's a harder 3 × 3 magic square problem. A prime square is one that uses only primes. An infinity of order-3 prime magic squares can probably be constructed with nine distinct primes, but which one has the lowest magic constant? If 1 is considered a prime, as it sometime was around 1900, the lowest constant is 111:

7	61	43
73	37	1
31	13	67

Today 1 is not called a prime. What prime magic square of order 3, using nine distinct primes that exclude 1, has the lowest constant? The number 2, the only even prime, cannot be used because all rows or diagonals with three odd primes would have an odd sum, whereas any row containing 2 would have an even sum. The answer to this question is not well known. You'll find the square in the next answer section.

35 THE WISDOM OF SOLOMON

Solutions to the Solomon puzzles follow:

1. A solution was provided by the graph in the previous answers section.

2. Shown below is one of many solutions to the Solomon magic star question. The magic constant (which can vary) is here 46.

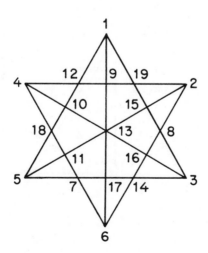

3. The pattern contains 56 triangles, and 156 quadrilaterals. Of the quadrilaterals, 57 are convex, 36 are nonconvex and uncrossed, and 63 are crossed. (A crossed quadrilateral is one with two opposite sides that intersect.) I don't know how many pentagons (crossed and uncrossed) the pattern contains, and I don't even want to know!

Anneli Lax writes:

From one of my math-anxious students, I learned the following method of counting the triangles in such complicated figures.

a. To each "small" triangle, i.e. one that contains no interior segments, assign a symbol. E.g., A for the one with vertices 1, 12, 9; B for the one with vertices 1, 9, 19; etc. Mark those triangles with their assigned symbols.

b. Assign symbols to all remaining convex polygons that have no interior segments. In this figure, there are six quadrilaterals in the middle, call them M: 12, 9, 13, 10; N: 19, 9, 13, 15; etc.

c. Look for triangles consisting of two already named subpolygons; and name them with the symbols of their composite parts, e.g., AB for 1, 12, 19; AM for 1, 10, 13; etc.

d. Look for triangles consisting of three subpolygons and name them with 3 symbols. Do same for four, etc... until list seems complete. Check list for duplicates.

4. John H. Conway first raised this curious question, and proved that the answer is yes. He also proved that the complete graph for six points is the highest-order complete graph that can be modeled without containing a knot. See "Knots and Links in Spatial Graphs," by Conway and C.M. Gordon, in the *Journal of Graph Theory*, Vol. 7 (1983), pages 445–453.

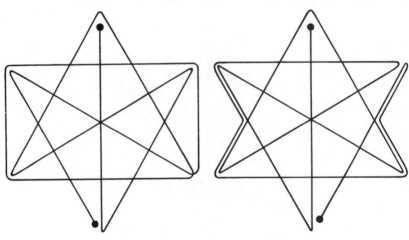

35

5. If doubling along line segments is permitted, and the path is confined to the lines, the illustration on the facing page, left, shows one of many possible ways to traverse the graph with a minimum-length path.

If one is allowed to go outside the graph, doubling along line segments is not necessary, and the path can be shortened as shown on the facing page, right.

6. The equilateral triangle is formed like this:

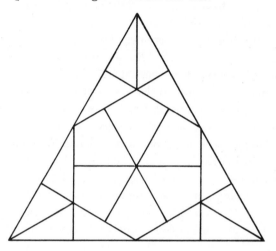

If we divide the kite shapes into halves, we see that the pieces consist of 24 right triangles of sides 1, $\sqrt{3}$ and a hypotenuse of 2. The area is $\frac{1}{2}\sqrt{3}$. The total area is therefore 24 times the area of the triangle, or $12\sqrt{3}$. To form a square, the square's side would have to be $\sqrt{12\sqrt{3}}$, a length not obtainable by any combination of sides of the pieces. A similar argument excludes the regular hexagon, although the pieces *will* form irregular convex hexagons.

7. The nine-move solution for Solomon solitaire, starting with a central hole, was found by Kathy Jones, whose company Kadon Enterprises, makes and sells the Solomon board game. The moves are: 14-10, 8-12, 19-10-14-16, 18-10-19-13, 1-8-18-10-1, 2-4, 9-3-5, 6-4, 1-10. If any reader finds a shorter solution, I would be pleased to get it.

35

36 THANG, THE PLANET EATER

The only possible last step is for Thang to toss away ten planets on the tenth day, then eat $\frac{1}{11}$ of no planets. Working backward, one finds that there were 100 planets at the start. The problem has endless variants. For example, change the fraction to $\frac{1}{13}$ and the starting number becomes 144 and the number of days goes to 12.

Problems of this sort—finding integral solutions to equations—belong to a branch of number theory called Diophantine analysis. The best known puzzle of this type involves five men, a monkey, and a supply of coconuts. It was the topic of Ben Ames Williams's short story "Coconuts" in *The Saturday Evening Post* (October 9, 1926). I have a chapter about it in *The Second Scientific American Book of Mathematical Puzzles and Diversions*.

Anyone familiar with my short story "Thang" will recall that while Thang was eating the Earth he was picked up and swallowed by a larger four-dimensional creature. I can now reveal for the first time that the beast who swallowed Thang somewhat resembled what we call a cow, only it had three heads and twelve arms. It is impossible to describe or imagine the beast because we are unable to visualize objects in dimensions higher than three.

As soon as Thang realized he had been swallowed by a hypercow, he curled himself up into a tight little ball. In the warmth and darkness of the hypercow's stomach, he fell asleep. When he woke the next day the hypercow was gone.

36

FOURTH ANSWERS

1 RIDDLE OF THE SPHINX

A recursive formula for a function of n, where n can take integer values, is one that tells you how to find the value of the function for any given n, provided you know its values for integers below n. Recursive formulas or procedures can be used to calculate successive values of the function by hand, or by using a computer. In this case you can calculate the number of left and right sphinxes by the following recursive procedures:

1. The number of L-sphinxes on day n is obtained by adding the number of L-sphinxes on the previous day $(n-1)$ to three times the number of R-sphinxes on the previous day. In algebraic terms:

$$L(n) = L(n-1) + 3R(n-1).$$

[Here $L(i)$ and $R(i)$ denote the number of left and right forms, respectively, on the ith day.]

2. The number of R-sphinxes on day n is obtained by adding the number of R-sphinxes on the previous day to three times the number of L-sphinxes on the previous day. Algebraically:

$$R(n) = R(n-1) + 3L(n-1).$$

A nonrecursive formula is one that does not require knowledge of the previous cases. You just plug the value of n into the formula and it gives the answer. Having observed in the previous answer section that the total number of sphinxes is 4^n and the difference between left and right forms is 2^n, we can easily find the two nonrecursive formulas for sphinx growth:

1

The number of *L*-sphinxes in the *n*th generation is

$$2^{n-1}\left[2^n + (-1)^n\right].$$

The number of *R*-sphinxes in the *n*th generation is

$$2^{n-1}\left[2^n - (-1)^n\right].$$

S. W. Golomb discovered the sphinx and gave the name *rep-tile* to all polygons that can be cut into *n* identical replicas of the original shape. Some Golomb rep-tiles split into two replicas, some into three, some into five or more. The sphinx is the only known pentagon that splits into four. If you can discover another, Professor Golomb would like to know about it! You can learn more about rep-tile theory and some of its fascinating unsolved problems by reading Chapter 19 of my book *The Unexpected Hanging and Other Mathematical Diversions*.

3 ON TO CHARMIAN

The CHAIRMAN is A RICH MAN.

When I first wrote about the game with ten cards, based on monotonic subsequences, I did not know it had already been solved by Frank Harary, Bruce Sagan, and David West. The first player can always win by taking a five on his first move. In the reverse game, the first player wins by taking a two. This is proved in their unpublished paper, "Computer-Aided Analysis of Monotonic Sequence Games."

In this paper the authors consider games based on a generalization of the Erdös-Szekeres theorem. The generalized theorem asserts that if *N* and *M* are non-negative integers, any sequence of at least $NM + 1$ distinct integers must contain an increasing subsequence of length $N + 1$, or a decreasing subsequence of length $M + 1$. The authors could not find a general strategy for standard or reverse two-person games based on this theorem. It is not yet known whether the first or second player has the win in a game with 17 cards ($M = N = 4$) bearing numbers 1 through 17, when players seek to achieve (or avoid) obtaining a monotonic (increasing or decreasing) subsequence of five numbers.

For a general analysis of games, with many marvelous examples, you might want to browse through the two volumes of *Winning Ways*, by Elwyn Berlekamp, John Conway, and Richard Guy.

6 AROUND THE SOLAR SYSTEM

The 3×4 array has a unique (except for symmetries) closed tour of only 5 segments. Three closed tours for the 4×4 are illustrated below. A detailed analysis of the 4×4 case can be found in *The Master Book of Mathematical Recreations*, by Fred Schuh (Dover 1968), Chapter 14.

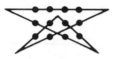

 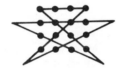

M.S. Klamkin proved that open paths on $n \times n$ arrays ($n > 2$) can be found with as few as $2n - 2$ segments (*American Mathematical Monthly*, Vol. 62, February 1955, page 124), and John Selfridge showed that $2n - 2$ segments are always necessary (*ibid*, Vol. 62, June 1955, page 443). Golomb and Selfridge, in their paper cited in the previous answer section, showed that the same result holds for closed paths if $n > 3$, and for paths that do not go outside the square's perimeter if $n > 5$. Little is known about minimum paths on nonsquare patterns of lattice points.

For some excellent new puzzles based on queen tours of lattice points see "Paths on arrays of dots," by Golomb, in the *Journal of Recreational Mathematics*, Vol. 1, July 1968, pages 154–156 (answered in Vol. 2, October 1969, pages 220–230) and "Dot Connection II," by Karl Scherer, *ibid*, Vol. 14, No. 3, 1981–82, page 232.

25

25 FLARP FLIPS ANOTHER FIVER

The following two letters were published in *Isaac Asimov's Science Fiction Magazine* (July 1986):

Dear Isaac,

In his always delightful column, Martin Gardner says that the origin of "raspberry" in the sense of a rude noise made with the lips is unknown. Since this will undoubtedly be my one and only chance ever to correct Martin Gardner, I hasten to do so.

The genesis is Cockney rhyming slang. You recall that this replaces a word with a phrase ending in a rhyme—for example, "plates of meat" for "feet" or "trouble and strife" for "wife"—and then often goes on to use only the first part of the phrase, thus turning "feet" into "plates" and so forth.

Well, a certain sound not supposed to be heard in polite society came to be called "raspberry tart." Later the reference moved anatomically upward . . . .

Best,

Poul Anderson
Orinda, CA

Dear Martin,

"Raspberry," in the sense of "Bronx cheer," is Cockney rhyming slang: raspberry tart.

John Brunner
South Petherton, Somerset,
England

29 HUSTLE OFF TO BUFFALO

We must show that the only real quadruples of infinite level are multiples of

$$(1) \qquad\qquad 1, \quad z, \quad z^2, \quad z^3,$$

where z is the real root of $z^3 - z^2 - z - 1 = 0$, and quadruples obtained from these by adding the same constant to each member.

Suppose the quadruple A, B, C, D has level > 8. By our previous results there will be only one local minimum and one local maximum and they will be next to each other. Suppose these are A and D. Then the sequence is monotone between A and D, i.e. it is nondecreasing or nonincreasing. The absolute differences are

$$a = |B - A|, \quad b = |C - B|, \quad c = |D - C|, \quad d = |D - A| = a + b + c;$$

the last equation follows from the fact that A, B, C, D is a monotone sequence. d is the largest among these four numbers. The smallest must be next to it (otherwise a, b, c, d would have non-adjacent extrema and could not have level > 7. If it happens to be c, rename the numbers by going from d the other way around the circle around which we may imagine the four numbers to be written. This makes the local minimum into a. There are no other local minima, hence

(4) $$0 < a < b < c < d.$$

The first inequality holds because our original quadruple had level > 6 and hence contained no equal numbers.

The next set of absolute differences is

(5)
$$a' = b - a, \quad b' = c - b,$$
$$c' = d - c = a + b, \quad d' = d - a = b + c.$$

Here we used the fact that $d = a + b + c$. By (4) d' is the largest of these numbers. Since we are still above level 6, the smallest must be next to it. We see that $a' < c'$, so a' must be the smallest, and b' and c' are neither local minima nor maxima. Therefore the inequalities (4) hold for the primed quantities also, and we can obtain the next set of absolute differences by applying the formulas (5) again. This will continue as long as we are above level 6.

The matrix form for the first three equations in (5) is

(6)
$$\begin{pmatrix} a' \\ b' \\ c' \end{pmatrix} = \begin{pmatrix} -1 & 1 & 0 \\ 0 & -1 & 1 \\ 1 & 1 & 0 \end{pmatrix} \begin{pmatrix} a \\ b \\ c \end{pmatrix};$$

the fourth is always the sum of the other three.

Denote the above "differencing" matrix by D and recall that for the special vector $v_1 = \begin{pmatrix} 1 \\ z \\ z^2 \end{pmatrix}$, see (1) above, differencing had the effect of transforming v_1 into

$$\begin{pmatrix} z - 1 \\ z^2 - z \\ z^3 - z^2 \end{pmatrix} = (z - 1) \begin{pmatrix} 1 \\ z \\ z^2 \end{pmatrix} = (z - 1)v_1.$$

29

Indeed, when we multiply v_1 by D, we find

$$Dv_1 = \begin{pmatrix} -1 & 1 & 0 \\ 0 & -1 & 1 \\ 1 & 1 & 0 \end{pmatrix} \begin{pmatrix} 1 \\ z \\ z^2 \end{pmatrix} = \begin{pmatrix} z - 1 \\ z^2 - z \\ z + 1 \end{pmatrix},$$

and since $z^3 - z^2 - z - 1 = 0$, the third component $z + 1 = z^3 - z^2$.

A non-zero vector v with the property that $Dv = \lambda v$, where λ is a scalar, is called an *eigenvector* of D with *eigenvalue* λ. The effect of multiplying a vector many times by a matrix D can best be studied by means of eigenvectors. We sketch the procedure below; for more details, consult books on linear algebra. In our case the eigenvector with components $1, z, z^2$ has eigenvalue $\lambda = z - 1$, where z is a root of the cubic $z^3 - z^2 - z - 1 = 0$. If we use the real root (see Third Answers section), then $\lambda_1 = z_1 - 1 \approx 1.839 \cdots - 1 = .839 \cdots < 1$, and the corresponding eigenvector v_1 has components $1, z_1, z_1^2$. Thus for the vector v_1 repeated multiplication by D has the same effect as repeated multiplication by the scalar $\lambda_1 = .839 \ldots$. In particular, the more times we multiply v_1 by D, the closer we get to the 0-vector $[0, 0, 0]^T$. (The T indicates that this vector is a column, even though we wrote it as a row.)

If one uses complex numbers one can find two other eigenvectors v_2, v_3 with eigenvalues $\lambda_2 = z_2 - 1$, $\lambda_3 = z_3 - 1$, where z_2, z_3 are the other two (complex) roots of our cubic. Both have absolute value $\approx 1.54 > 1$.

How do these special vectors, which behave very simply under multiplication by D, tell us what happens to a general vector under repeated multiplications by D? The answer is surprisingly simple. Any vector $[a, b, c]^T$ is a sum of multiples of the three eigenvectors. Each application of D multiplies the magnitude of v_2 and v_3 by $1.54 \ldots$, a number > 1, so unless their coefficients are 0 in the representation $\alpha v_1 + \beta v_2 + \gamma v_3$ of the vector $[a, b, c]^T$, the size of our vectors will sooner or later start to grow and go to infinity. Taking absolute differences of their components can not lead to such a result; for, once the numbers are ≥ 0, none of the differences can be larger than the largest of the numbers. We conclude that, if the set of second differences of our original numbers do not form a constant multiple of the quadruple (4), we must at some stage get below level 7, at which time taking absolute differences need no longer be equivalent to multiplying by the matrix D and the process comes to an end.

The first known appearance of our problem is in the Italian journal Periodico di Matematiche, (4) 7 (1937), pp. 25–30, where it is attributed to E. Ducci. It is discussed in Ross Honsberger's *Ingenuity in Mathematics*, New Mathematical Library vol. 23, Ch. 10. Among the periodical articles about the problem we mention the ones by Robert Miller in the American Math. Monthly, Vol. 85 (1978), pp. 183–85, and by Leroy Meyers in Crux Mathematicorum, Vol. 8 (1982), pp. 262–266. Meyers cites 22 references.

31 PUZZLE FLAGS ON MARS

The magic constant 177 is the lowest possible for a square of distinct primes, not including 1 as a prime. The earliest reference I know on this square is Joseph Madachy's *Mathematics on Vacation* (Scribner's, 1966), page 95, where it is credited to Rudolph Ondrejka.

17	113	47
89	59	29
71	5	101

Can a prime magic square of order 3 be constructed with nine primes in arithmetic progression? Yes, and again the number of such squares is almost certainly infinite. The one with the lowest constant is

1669	199	1249
619	1039	1459
829	1879	409

that magic constant is 3,117, and the common difference of the arithmetic progression is 210.

Is it possible to construct an order-3 magic square with *consecutive* primes? This is the most challenging unsolved problem in magic square theory. Squares of consecutive primes have been constructed for orders 4, 5, and 6, and there is even a consecutive-prime square starting with 3 that is 35 × 35 (the smallest size possible for such a square). But the order-3, starting with any number, has such tight constraints that so far it has eluded all computer efforts toward a solution. I will give $100 to the first person who constructs one.